# Unwavering Faith

## A True Story Of Trusting God Through Cancer & Never Losing Hope

Rachele Wright

*Published by*

Wright On Target, LLC.

ISBN: 978-1-7336478-0-9

Unless otherwise noted, scripture quotations are from the
King James Version Bible

# DEDICATION

This book is dedicated to my husband Norm. He inspires me everyday to be more than I ever thought I could be. He loves the Lord more than any person I know, which makes me love him even more. I am so blessed that we have had almost 30 years to grow in our marriage and I look forward to serving the Lord together for many years to come.

# CONTENTS

# ACKNOWLEDGMENTS

I would like to thank my wonderful family and friends for all of their prayers and support. You all have been such a tremendous blessing to me on this journey.

~~~~~

To all of the incredible medical team that has cared for me through this crazy ride of treatments, surgeries and trials…. your support, care and dedication is priceless and very much appreciated.

~~~~~

The most heartfelt thanks I could ever give goes to my Lord and Savior Jesus Christ. His sacrifice at the whipping post and on the cross is what makes my healing possible – In Him, is my faith unwavering.

# CHAPTER 1
## HOW IT ALL STARTED

About 2 hours ago, my world as I know it has changed.

I received a phone call from my gynecologist's office and they informed me that I have  CANCER.

That is the scariest word I NEVER thought I would hear about myself.  There are no traces of cancer on either side of my family, so I am definitely a trailblazer.  Lucky me, right?  Just trying to throw some humor in my life right now because I have been walking around in a sort of "trance" for the last 2 hours.

Ever since I received the phone call, I have almost felt

numb. How did this happen? Were there warning signs I missed? Actually, I need to put down how the whole thing may have started just for the record. I don't want to forget anything. I believe I need to quickly go back about 6 months to really start at the beginning.

I have always been a person with a heavy menstrual flow when it came to monthly periods, so when they started getting a little heavier, I wasn't too alarmed. Everyone said that as you get older they get heavier before they get lighter and then you eventually go through menopause. No big deal, right? I am at the right age, 44, so it seemed to make sense. I also noticed that I had to get up every night for the past 6 months to pee. The only other time in my life that this happened to me was when I was pregnant. Looking back, I should have gone to the doctor for a checkup right then since that was abnormal for me. That would have been the smart thing to do.

I also hadn't been to the gynecologist in about 3 years. My husband, Norm, has his own business and I work for him. Therefore, I always felt guilty to take too much time off for personal reasons.

I always thought of cancer as a hereditary thing, or something that happened to people who lived an unhealthy lifestyle for their entire adult life. That's definitely not me! I eat healthy and workout. It truly NEVER crossed my mind that I could ever get cancer. It's so surreal to even say that word about myself!

## The Warning Signs I Missed:

In retrospect, there were some signs I overlooked. One indicator might have been the shortening of my cycle. But, probably the most upsetting for me was the weight gain. I had become a bit of a workout fanatic over the years. About 17 years ago, I had worked my butt off to lose 30 pounds, and I certainly was not thrilled with gaining around 8 pounds in the past six months. I had managed to maintain my weight for 16 years and all of a sudden I was hit with this unexpected weight gain. I had been eating healthy and working out consistently, but was gaining weight anyway. So I started working out harder—no help.

Frustrating didn't even begin to cover how this made me feel. I am one of those freaks that weigh myself every morning too. I always tracked my weight to make sure I didn't let it get out of control and watching it slowly rise was a bit of a bummer, to say the least. My friends all said this was the start of pre-menopause. They all said that it happened to them too. So I started working out even harder. Still nothing. I had no idea what else I would have to do to lose weight besides quitting my job and spending my entire day working out and eating only lettuce.

While this was unusual to me, these changes also could be explained as part of the aging process of a woman of 44.

Then came what I like to call the "hemorrhage day". My daughter had just graduated high school and my husband and I were going to several graduation parties each weekend for all of her friends. This went on from May through July. On this particular night, June 25, 2011, we were at our first of two parties we would be attending.

We had arrived pretty late to the first party because I had been working in the yard all day clearing woods. Our yard has woods at the back end and I wanted more usable area for our yard, so I spent every weekend for several summers clearing weeds, chopping down small trees, digging up roots, and digging up the garbage thrown in our woods by our builders who didn't feel like properly disposing of their building materials. It was great fun, let me tell you.

Needless to say, it was high impact manual labor for a 44-year old woman, but I really wanted the area cleared. My husband said I was just being a "hard-head" for not paying someone to do it. I have always liked to do my yard work myself. So, on this particular day I spent a lot more time chopping down trees with my dull ax than any other weekend that I had worked on clearing the woods. Many of the previous weekends involved more digging, but this day was all about chopping trees and jarring the heck out of my body.

Looking back, it was probably a good thing because I think it may have disrupted the tumor or whatever makes you bleed A LOT!

We arrived at the first party ready to relax, eat and socialize with all our friends. I no sooner got done eating dinner when I stood up to hug my good friend's son that had come over to say hello, when I felt a MASSIVE gush (and I am not person alarmed by a lot of blood). My Capri pants made of a really thick jean material were saturated pretty far down my leg in a matter of seconds. I ran to the bathroom, and wouldn't you know it, there was a line of people! The people who were talking to me while I waited (it seemed like 2 hours) probably thought I was on some kind of drugs because I couldn't even hear a word they were saying. I was so focussed on keeping my legs pressed tightly together so no one could see the blood.

As soon as it was my turn, I practically sprinted into the bathroom and I shoved about 3 rolls of toilet paper in my pants to try and soak things up. And I couldn't believe I actually had a tampon in my purse when it wasn't even my period time. I came out of the bathroom and speed-walked to my husband and told him we had to "LEAVE NOW!" (you know the way you can say it where your eyes are bulging out of your head so he knows to get the heck up and outta there fast).

We got into the car and my husband was horrified when I showed him how soaked I was. Every woman knows how squeamish guys are about anything that has to do with a period, so I have to give him credit that he kept it together. It was then that I thought I was going to pass out -- probably because of how scared I was, not from the blood loss. Nothing like this had ever happened before, so my mind was racing. Norm was just as alarmed as I was. We went straight home where I could see that there was still a substantial amount of blood flowing. About 15 minutes later, it had slowed down to the point where a tampon and a large pad could handle it. So I got changed and we headed to the other party. Thankfully it had slowed down just enough to get me through the next two hours.

It was Saturday evening, therefore no doctor's offices were open, so there was no one to call for an appointment, and I didn't want to go to the emergency room. Over the rest of the weekend I bled pretty consistently...sorta like a really, really bad period. Looking back, I should have probably gone to the emergency room immediately and gotten the process started sooner, but quite honestly I didn't want to pay the $150 copay. I'm thinking maybe my thriftiness was not a good thing here.

I did call the gynecologist's office the minute they opened on Monday morning and they squeezed me in on Tuesday. I was seen by the Physicians Assistant, and upon examination, she said she could see what looked like a polyp on my cervix. She thought that that merited getting a saline sonohysterogram to see if I had other polyps in my uterus.

We had to wait over a week just to get approval from my medical insurance before we could even schedule the sonogram. Once they got the authorization approval, the gynecologist's office wanted me to wait until August (which was over a month) to schedule it. I definitely DID NOT want to wait that long! I told the scheduling person that I would take any appointment with any of their doctors to move this process along faster. I sat on hold for about 15 minutes while she looked through the schedule. Eventually she was able to schedule the sonogram in two weeks.

By the time I was seen for the sonogram, it had been over 3 weeks since my initial exam and pap smear --- which, by the way, did NOT COME BACK AS CANCER. Now that's scary! I actually had a cancerous tumor on my cervix/uterus at that moment—and I was not contacted that there was a problem with my pap smear.

This is a good reason to get your pap smear EVERY YEAR, and not every 3-5 years like I did! It was not a perfectly regular pap smear, but the doctor's didn't have a previous year pap smear to compare it with. The yearly exams that everyone always said I should have been getting, suddenly appeared to be more important than I had previously thought. The doctors were right. Definitely get a pap smear every year! Hard lesson learned.

Over the next few weeks I bled pretty consistently. Some days were worse than others, but there was no letting up for two weeks. Certain days there would be a heavy flow all day, and then other days it would slow down to almost a stop, and then kick up again in the evening. It was so confusing.

My doctor's office called me about 2 days before my sonogram (which, as I said, was already a three week wait) and asked if they could reschedule it to a later date because there was a scheduling error with their new computer software. They actually wanted to postpone the appointment. I was floored. I explained to the woman in scheduling that I had been bleeding for quite a while now and was very concerned. I thought it was already too long for me to wait to find out if there was something wrong...and I was not about to wait another week because of their scheduling mess-up. She eventually found something even sooner, and it was fortunately with the same Physician's Assistant I had seen before.

Women know their own bodies and I knew something wasn't quite right. As a person that had never missed a period in 25 years (besides pregnancy) and certainly never had mid-month severe bleeding for 14 days, I knew it was important to find the source of this problem because I had a feeling it was not going to be something good. I was thinking it would be more along the lines of needing a D&C or Ablation to fix polyps, or a cyst, or something to that nature. I definitely knew I needed to find out what the heck was going on in there. It just didn't seem like a simple change in hormones from pre-menopause. I think God was getting me prepared for this big news because even though I never even considered cancer, I started getting an ominous feeling, like a pit in my stomach, that this was something big.

I was so relieved when I finally got to the doctor's office the day of the saline sonohysterogram. No female on earth looks forward to an appointment where you are being humiliated and violated by devices that are probing your privates...but I just wanted to find out some truth. They conducted the sonogram and found at least 5 polyps in my uterus. The Physicians Assistant said I would need a D&C to have them removed. We scheduled the procedure right away. They had also done a biopsy of the lining of my uterus during the sonogram, which ended up being the biggest blessing in the world because that's when they had accidentally gotten some cells from the tumor.

**Getting the News:**

After an agonizing week of waiting, the Physicians Assistant called to tell me the news. I was on lunch break from work and ran to Walmart to grab a few items for home. As all of us working women know you have to make good use of every free minute. I had just walked in the store when my cell phone rang and I recognized the number as my gynecologist's office; I answered it immediately. The Physicians Assistant that I had now seen twice, informed me that the biopsy had identified Adenocarcinoma cells, which is a type of cancer.

There are no words to describe the temperature of the intense heat wave that rolled all the way down my body, from my head to my toes. The very first thought that went through my mind was that I was not going to be around to see my kids get married, which had never crossed my mind before. I have no clue why it was that thought exactly, but that was my very first thought. I know that no one on the face of the earth wants to hear the word cancer, but I came from a family that has no history of the disease anywhere, so "being shocked" is a huge understatement. This didn't even seem real. I frantically grabbed a pen and a ripped up piece of paper out of my purse and wrote down all the information given to me by the Physicians Assistant about the oncologist's office where she had already scheduled my appointment. The Physicians Assistant was very nice and apologetic that she had to do this on the phone, but she wanted me to get help from the oncologist as soon as possible. I still don't know how I held it together through that conversation.     I hung up with her and, in my numbness, I proceeded to walk around Walmart to look for the items on my grocery list.  I walked in circles for about 60 seconds and kept staring at the list that I was holding in my shaking hands.    I finally realized that I couldn't remember where anything was in the store.  I had shopped at this store a million times and I knew the store like the back of my hand, but I was incapable of remembering anything at that moment.  I gave up and walked out.  As I was walking out I called my husband.

I had been working for my husband for the past 11 years at his Advertising/Marketing firm.  So, since I had just left him about 10 minutes ago to run to the store, he was probably wondering why the heck I was calling him.  As I walked through the parking lot to get back to my car, my husband answered his cell phone and I tried as hard as I could to tell him, but I was crying so hard he couldn't even understand what I was saying.  When I was finally able to articulate words again, I told him what the Physicians Assistant had said and he was the amazingly supportive and calm husband he has always been.

You see, part of my story is a "love story" of how a couple that has always been crazy about each other can become even closer through a situation like mine --- one that you thought would be something you could never make it through without it tearing you apart. Actually, the exact opposite has happened. We have become closer than ever each and every year with God guiding us all the way.

I made it back to the office by talking to him on my phone the whole 10-minute ride. I really don't remember much of the driving. I was completely on remote control. All I knew was that I needed to get to where my husband was. I ran into the building and hugged him for a really, really long time. He immediately started to reassure me that it was going to be fine.

I showed him all the information that the gynecologist's office gave me about the oncologist and the date of my appointment. He and I agreed that I needed to call my brother right away. My brother is a plastic surgeon and knows a lot of doctors in the area and I wanted to make sure I was going to the best oncologist I could find. Pittsburgh is well known for their expertise in the medical field, so I figured I could get a really good doctor.

I called my brother's cell phone because I knew I could leave a message with a nurse if he was in surgery. Fortunately I called when he was driving back to his office after surgery, so he called me back right away. He knew it must have been important since he knew I never called him during the work day because I never wanted to bother him when he was in surgery or seeing patients. He immediately asked me what type of cancer it was and inquired about all the additional clinical information they gave me. Of course I couldn't remember half of it, so he had me call the gynecologist's office and have them fax over the results of the biopsy and any other clinical information available.

I immediately called the gynecologist's office and the P.A. said she would fax all the clinical information over immediately. I must note that she was a very compassionate person through the entire ordeal --- starting with my initial exam, then the sonohysterogram, and even through the gut-wrenching call she had to make to tell me the dreaded news. I believe it is so important to have a person with a good bedside manner in the gynecological field in particular, because it is so uncomfortable to begin with for most women.

We received the fax within minutes and I called my brother back to convey the results. He told me he would make a call to a gynecologist friend and see if he would recommend this particular oncologist. He called me back a few hours later and said his friend said he would send his wife to this doctor if his wife was diagnosed with cancer. That was reassuring. Knowing I was going to an experienced oncologist gave me some hope. Sadly, my experience with this oncologist was not a positive one like I had hoped. But that story will unfold and be explained later.

## Mistake #1: Do as much research as possible on your doctor!

1. Research every doctor in which you schedule an appointment.

2. Find out about their experience and if they have high ratings with previous patients.

3. Do not take the word of one person or one colleague who is probably their friend.

My brother was extremely supportive and helpful and I knew he would try and educate me on any medical information he had regarding the cancer and try to make this whole experience less scary for me.

As Norm and I headed home from work a couple of hours later, it hit me --- we now had to go about the gut-wrenching task of telling our kids and parents and the rest of our family. I don't know about other people, but I was so upset about the news that I really didn't want to tell anyone else but my husband. It kind of felt like if I didn't tell anyone, then it wouldn't be totally real. It was almost a little embarrassing. Not like I had any control over getting this, but I didn't want the whole world to know. I know that sounds weird, but I really didn't want this kind of attention. This much attention was really going to put me out of my comfort zone. I knew I was going to need the support of my family and friends, but who wants to be the source of such bad news.

I have always tried to live my life with a positive attitude and tried to view all things from God's Divine perspective if at all possible. So I had to apply that perspective to this experience as well. Knowing that God has a wonderful, divine plan for my life, I knew that I could trust in Him, and He would work all things for good, since I am one of His children. I kept trying to cling to this fact and focus on God's grace, which will bring me through anything, instead of dwelling on my fears.

But I was still having a hard time figuring out how to break this news to those closest to me without breaking down. Here is another instance where having an awesome, strong and loving husband was an enormous blessing. We talked on our way home from work that first day, and Norm and I agreed that he would make sure that when he told our kids and close family and friends that he would reassure everyone that I was fine and it would all work out because God was in control of our lives. This made me feel so much better since I never wanted to be a source of pain for anyone close to me. On the contrary, my entire goal since I became a wife and Mom was to make my family happy and be the source of encouragement and God's true joy.

There is no doubt that telling my kids was the worst part of the whole thing. When we got home, they were out in the front yard of our house playing with our granddaughter. Norm asked them to come inside because we wanted to talk to them about something. They immediately asked if there was something wrong. We, of course, lied and said no. I still don't know how they immediately knew something was wrong.

I forced a smile and held back tears while Norm was telling them the news because I didn't want them to think I was freaking out inside. Which, in reality, it felt like someone was scraping a hot knife through my stomach. We all sat and talked for a long time and then painfully tried to go about having a normal night. I told them to go to the gym and do everything they would normally do because I was going to be fine. I was determined not to make my kids unhappy and think this was a death sentence.

When you get life-changing news, everyone reacts differently and I believed it was important to try and keep things as normal as possible. I already had such a sense of guilt that I was making my family go through this. My daughter was 18, and my son was 20 at the time and this was way too young for them to think about losing their mom. So, I insisted that this was going to be taken care of, and we would just take this one step at a time and God will bring us through it all. I was saying all of this not just to convince my family but to convince myself as well.

I have to go off on a mini sidebar here momentarily and express how extremely blessed beyond measure I am to have the support from everyone in my family through all the years of this journey. My husband, my son Brennan, my daughter Laney, and my granddaughter have been my inner circle of strength for 7 years. I love them all more than I could ever express with words and I am so thankful that God has allowed me the precious privilege to be Norm's wife, My children's Mom, and my granddaughter's

"Grammy" for so long. I am thankful for every second! I am also thankful to my extended family: My Mom, my Dad, my two awesome brothers and their wonderful wives and children. Also, my husband's caring parents, sisters and their children too. I don't think this book would truly reflect who I am without adding how important my family is to me and how much I have relied on them these past 7 years. I have additionally been blessed with the best friends a person could ask for. They have all supported us both through constant prayer and many other ways. Thank you all for being so wonderful and encouraging all these years.

# CHAPTER 2
# THE FIRST VISIT WITH THE ONCOLOGIST

I had my initial visit with the oncologist only 4 days after the call from my gynecologist's office. They wanted me to get in there as quickly as possible. I remember the car ride down with my husband. I was so anxious, I felt like I wanted to throw up. The doctor's office was just outside of downtown Pittsburgh, so we had to sit through morning rush hour traffic to get there, which is always a pleasant hour of inching down the highway. When I finally got there and went in, the office seemed nice enough and I had to fill out what felt like a book of paperwork.

When I went back to the exam room, the nurse gave me the lovely paper gown that all of us women are familiar with, just like at the regular gynecologist office, since the doctor was a gynecological oncologist/surgeon.

In the exam room, the doctor proceeded to ask me a few questions , and then he did the gynecological exam. During the exam, I heard him say to the nurse that he saw the tumor. That was the first time I heard the word tumor, and I'm going to be honest...it really freaked me out. How could that be a word that someone was saying about me. I think the whole "surreal aspect" of being diagnosed with cancer goes on for a long time...at least for me it has.

I kept thinking, " Is this really happening to me?" As soon as my mind would go to those negative places I would immediately keep thinking on how God will never leave us nor forsake us. I really needed the comfort of God's protective, loving arms through this entire experience. I still do today!

After the exam, I got dressed and met the doctor and my husband in his office to discuss his findings, the biopsy, and what steps he wanted to take next. He said from the size of the tumor he believed it was only Stage 1 cervical/ uterine cancer. He believed that we could stop this with no problem and that I would be fine.

It was his opinion that I should have a radical hysterectomy followed by radiation therapy once I was healed from the surgery. He explained that the surgery would include removal of my uterus, fallopian tubes, ovaries, cervix and all the lymph nodes in the area.

He then stated that he wanted to do the surgical procedure using a mechanical surgical system so that there would be less scarring on my abdomen. I had never heard of that surgical system before but I thought this sounded like great news. Who wants extra scarring if you can avoid it?

**Mistake # 2: Research the heck out of the surgical procedure that your surgeon is recommending!**

1. Make sure you are aware of the risks and the possible permanent side effects.

2. Definitely find out how experienced the surgeon is at performing that particular surgery !

3. Find out how long that particular surgical procedure has been used.

I will explain later how this was not the right surgery for me.!

## Mistake #3: GET A SECOND OPINION!

1. GET A SECOND OPINION! GET A SECOND OPINION! I can't say it enough!

2. Never take the word of one man. You should always get another doctor's perspective with a new diagnosis.

3. Whether it's surgery, chemotherapy or radiation; get a second opinion on what steps they would recommend next.

The oncologist scheduled the surgery for the following Thursday at a hospital in the Pittsburgh Area. I really didn't know anyone who had ever been admitted to that hospital, so I had no real opinion of it. The doctor liked to do his surgeries at this hospital, so I didn't question it. Just like how I didn't question his choice of surgery method, either. I believe now that I was still so shocked at my diagnosis that I was doing anything this oncologist told me to do because I felt like I had no options. I literally did not question anything. I get so angry at myself now for being so apathetic, but at the time I thought he was my only option.

**Mistake #4: Research the hospital where your surgery will take place!**

1.  Find out as many details about the hospital as possible!

2.  Research patient reviews and complaints.

3.  Research any lawsuits filed against the hospital or their doctors.

Do not leave anything to chance. You deserve the best care possible!

The following week was crazy. I had a ton of work to do at my job to get prepared to be out of work for over a week. I was not worried about vacation time, since I had a lot of vacation time saved up, but my responsibilities at work included handling all the finances, so I wanted to make sure all taxes, accounts payable and payroll were all handled ahead of time.

The fact that I was so busy was kind of good for me since it didn't allow me a lot of time to dwell on my circumstances and I really made a concerted effort to not feel sorry for myself. It's a good thing to keep busy. I would never recommend sitting at home and obsessing over things if you can avoid it. If you don't work, then maybe find ways to do things for others, if you are physically able. Possibly volunteering with an organization that you are passionate about. Do not neglect taking good care of your body and eating right, but being selfless and helping others is a great idea for anyone. There are so many people in need in our world. Many people are in need our own country, and in our own neighborhoods. Nothing makes me feel better than giving back.

## The Surgery:

The day prior to the surgery, my surgical oncologist, let's now call him Dr. No, had me do a cleanse similar to the type that people do for a colonoscopy. I'm not exactly sure why, but I guess he didn't want anything at all in my intestines for the surgery. I was not allowed to eat the day of the cleanse, only clear liquids, and then nothing after midnight.

I had to be at the hospital at 6 a.m. the day of the surgery, so we left the house at 5 a.m. to make sure we avoided all the rush hour traffic. Fortunately, we made really good time, and we arrived early. The staff got me prepped and in a hospital gown and ready for the surgery by 6:30 a.m.

Then we waited...and waited...and waited.

I know it's common to experience delays when it comes to surgery because there are emergency cases that come up and must be put ahead of scheduled surgeries, but I was still waiting at 3 p.m. when my surgeon finally came into my room. He said he would like to postpone the surgery until the next day because it was late. I was in shock! After almost 2 days of no food and 16 hours of no fluid, he wanted me to go home and fast another day and come back and try this again. There was no way I wanted to wait that long. I asked if it was possible if we could go ahead with the surgery. He reluctantly agreed. (Which, in retrospect, I now regret because I think he was tired and not ready to do his best.) He had the surgical staff bring me back to the Operating Room and we got everything rolling.

After the surgery, I remember waking up and immediately asking for my glasses because I am so blind without them that it makes me feel even more disoriented than the anesthesia that was now wearing off. They called for my husband to bring the glasses back to the post-operative area and then transported me to my room soon after since it was already after 9 p.m.

The surgery had taken over 5 hours. I remember being so relieved that it was over and knowing the cancer was out of my body. My husband was relieved that I made it through the surgery alive. I was in quite a bit of pain, since I was in surgery for 5 hours, but I was glad that part was over and now I could begin healing process and put this whole experience behind me.

My husband had NEVER missed one appointment of mine and never wanted me to go through anything alone. However, on this particular night, he had to go home to help my daughter fill out all of her online applications for college loans because the deadline was midnight. We had all been so preoccupied with everything going on with me, that we didn't even think to check on that date.

Laney, our daughter, reminded us the night before my surgery, and Norm said he would run home right after the surgery and help her fill out the financial information and then return to the hospital to stay with me overnight. Since the surgery had been scheduled for 6 a.m., we figured he had plenty of time. I never even imagined the surgery would be delayed 8 hours and the surgery itself would go on for 5 hours. Dr. No never indicated the length of the surgery to myself or to Norm. We had no idea the surgery would be that long.

It was after 10 p.m. at this point and Norm had to leave to get the forms done by the midnight deadline. I told him to stay home and just go to bed after they finished and come back in the morning since it was going to be ridiculous to drive back to the hospital that late.

**Mistake #5: Don't ever stay overnight at the hospital alone!**

1. The patient always needs an advocate.

2. Since the patient is usually in pain and kind of "out of it" after surgery, they need someone alert to watch out for them.

3. The patient needs someone to who can stand up for them if they are not receiving the proper care.

I can remember being at the hospital alone after surgery and calling my nurse to my room and telling her I was in a lot of pain. She said that the new Medical Intern that was on duty had only ordered NSAIDS for me for pain. If you don't know what that is --- it is basically the same as Ibuprofen (Non-Steroidal Anti-Inflammatory Drugs). I really couldn't believe that this could be a standard pain medicine administered after a 5 hour surgery where the surgeon had just removed my uterus, fallopian tubes, ovaries and cervix, plus all the lymph nodes in the area. Additionally, I had not had a drink of water since 10 p.m. the day before.

It had been about 26 hours without fluids and I could barely speak because my mouth was so dry. The nurse gave me a very small cup of ice and said that was all I was allowed to have. I thought it was standard to have fluids given to a patient via their IV after surgery if they were not allowed to drink water, but my IV was not being used AT ALL! No fluids (or anything else) were hooked up to it. She just injected the NSAIDS directly into my IV port that was on the back of my left hand.

The NSAIDS did absolutely nothing for the pain, and since I was not getting any fluids, the dryness was getting worse. I'm not saying they should have let me chug a quart of water, but fluid management after surgery seems to be critically important for proper healing. I'm thinking that no fluids for approximately 30 hours might not be the best idea! I'm no doctor, but that seems ridiculous.

I sat there watching TV, trying not to move one micron, because the pain was extremely intense when I moved AT ALL! Finally, at around 3 a.m. I couldn't take it any longer and I paged the nurse again, and again. I had to press the "Nurse" button several times to get an answer at all. It actually took her about a half hour to finally come to my room. I asked her again if there was anything else for my pain, and she said she would ask the on-duty doctor again. I never did hear back from her regarding that doctor. Finally at 4 a.m., she came back to my room and told me that the Physicians Assistant that worked for Dr. No had called in to my floor at the hospital to check on me. She had to wake up to feed her baby anyway, so she thought she would check on my condition.

The Physicians Assistant asked the nurse which pain meds I was being given. The nurse told her the type of NSAID she had administered. The Physicians Assistant was appalled that I was not getting any relief for the pain and ordered her to get into my room and give me some morphine immediately. I'm pretty sure the Physicians Assistant assumed that the surgeon or the hospital would have already had a bag of fluids running in my IV, so she didn't even ask about that.

Immediately after, the nurse came in and told me what the Physicians Assistant had said, and she immediately injected the morphine directly into my IV port on the back of my hand. I was so happy to hear that I might have a little relief from the pain so I could possibly sleep for at least an hour. I was completely exhausted but the pain would not allow me to fall asleep.

Within a very short time, I started feeling horrendous. I was so dizzy and lightheaded that I could barely see or hear. The next thing I remember is a large group of people in my room and my bed was tilted up so that the foot of the bed was way up in the air toward the ceiling, and my head was almost on the ground. Needless to say I awoke very confused. I guess I had briefly lost consciousness. I looked at my nurse with a really confused look. The nurse, on the other hand, looked like she was in an absolute panic. My nurse turned to me said that I really gave them as scare! She said my pulse and blood pressure went dangerously low and alarms were going off like crazy.

Again, I know I'm not a doctor, but injecting morphine directly into a vein when the person had been without fluids for 30 hours seems to be ill-advised, to say the least. Now that there was a team of people in the room, someone had the bright idea of hooking up some fluids. I heard the nurse say I was not allowed to have any more morphine because I obviously had a reaction to it. Not that it was their mess-up at all????!!!

I honestly wondered if this nurse had ever taken care of a person after a surgery before.

So... since there was no more morphine allowed, I just had to deal with the pain!

I know God was with me that night as He always is, because I never felt the slightest bit of fear through the whole thing. That surprises most people, but I am happy to say that God must have been giving me a ton of grace through the whole experience, because I truly had no fear. I did have severe pain, but never any fear! I actually prayed and talked to God the whole night because I felt like

I no one was there to help or comfort me. Then I remembered the verse, (Hebrews 13:5) for He hath said, I will never leave thee, nor forsake thee. I knew He was with me and I didn't feel alone anymore.

The night did go very, very slowly because of the intense pain. I also found out that the only thing on TV late at night are infomercials. Not the most entertaining television! But God was with me and continually comforted me and gave me the overwhelming sense that it would all be okay and He was in control.

I am including these negative medical experiences, not to scare anyone, but so no one else has to go through the same things. I am giving everyone a very large "HEADS UP" on this. Don't make the same mistakes I did. Please make sure someone can stay with you if at all possible. If not, please be advised to bring your justified complaint of your care to someone else at the hospital if things don't seem right.

DO NOT BE LIKE ME: I just sat there quietly enduring it. It's good to be your own advocate! And be assured: NOT everyone is good at their job in the medical field, just like all other fields of work.

The next morning my husband was back at 8 a.m. and I told him about my eventful night and detailed everything that had happened. He felt really guilty that he had not been there. This was a very pivotal moment for him. I believe to this day he still feels guilty about it because he won't even let me go to the most minor of appointments without him. I have repeatedly assured him it was not his fault, but he is determined that he will never let a inept staff member have such a negative impact on my care again because he will be there to prevent it.

I can't even express what a huge sense of relief it was having my husband there in the morning. He has always been my biggest protector and such a loving husband! He could tell I was in a lot of pain. He was so sweet and tried everything to comfort me.

About 10 a.m., the new nurse on duty came in and said that it had been over 12 hours since my surgery, so I had to get up and walk around the room to reduce the risk of blood clots. I was very fearful hearing this because I was doing everything in my power to not move a muscle. I didn't even move to a new position on the bed because any movement invoked such intense pain. But, I figured if that's what I need to do to have proper healing, then let's do this thing! I would just have to grin and bear the pain.

Norm and the nurse helped to spin my feet from the foot of the bed over to the side, so that way I would be in position for them to both pull me up by my hands. So we counted to 3 and they began to pull me up. Well, that's the last thing I remember. When I woke up, I was back on the bed in the normal position. I had lost consciousness again! This was beginning to be a trend at this hospital. Not a good trend I might add.

Once I was conscious again, Norm and the nurse told me what happened. They explained that while they were gently pulling me up, my eyes rolled back in my head and my whole body became stiff as a board and I started falling backwards. I really wish I had a video of this. I know it was probably scary for them, but it had to be seriously funny to watch when it's yourself. Especially since the care I received at this hospital seemed to cause loss of consciousness more often than most hospitals.

The nurse then ran to find a doctor because she was really freaked out. Norm told me the rest of what happened once the nurse left the room. He said that when all this started, and I began to fall backwards, the nurse started frantically screaming "Oh My, Oh My, Oh My"! Norm had to actually calm HER down. He saw that I was breathing, so he told her I was going to be okay. I guess it was just a pain overload on my body, so my body decided to not be conscious for it.

Around 4:00 p.m. that day, my close friend that is a surgical nurse came to visit me. Once I told her everything that happened, she was horrified. She asked the nurse on duty if I could at least have some Vicodin for the pain so I could possibly get a little sleep that second night. The nurse asked the doctor and he gave the order for it, so I did get some sleep that second night.

## The After-Effects of the Surgery:

The next morning I was released to go home because I proved that I could get up and walk around the room. Once we got to the car, I remember asking my husband to not hit any bumps or potholes on the road because any car movement was really painful. I think he drove 15 mph the whole way home from downtown Pittsburgh. It took about an extra half hour at least to get home. My poor husband was so patient with me. I was never so happy to see my home.

By the second day, the effects of the surgery started to become painfully apparent. My abdomen looked like I was about 6-7 months pregnant because of the amount of swelling. My abdomen and upper thighs had turned intensely dark purple and black. I wish I had taken a picture of it. Over time, the swelling from my stomach migrated down to my upper thighs. They were huge. I had to wear loose dresses for about 2 months to cover up the massive swelling and also cover up the fact that I had a catheter bag strapped to my leg.

The hospital sent me home with a catheter and had given me instructions before I left the hospital on how to use it properly, such as emptying the bag that was strapped to my leg every couple of hours, and how to use the catheter at night with the larger bag that you hang next to the bed. I was very confused at why I still had the catheter. My doctor never told me I would have to wear a catheter home after the surgery, let alone for a minimum of 2 weeks. I had never known anyone that went home from the hospital with a catheter after a hysterectomy.

But again, since I had been in such a state of shock when I was diagnosed, that I didn't ask any questions regarding the surgery that my doctor picked for me. I was just going along with everything he told me to do like a robot.

I wish there was some way to go back in time and ask more questions and research what was going to be done to me in surgery and to definitely get a second opinion. It would have saved me so much pain and suffering, and spared me permanent side effects because of his choice. I had never asked if this surgery he chose for me using a mechanical surgical system would leave me with any permanent side effects, and I never asked how long the surgery would be, nor did I ask how much experience he had doing the surgery with this new technology.

The following week I returned to my oncologist's office. Dr. No gave me a small pamphlet to read, that he wrote, that explained the bladder issues that can occur after the hysterectomy he performed with that surgical system. It explained that the bladder will take some time to return to working order. Now let me tell you, I WOULD NEVER HAVE CHOSEN THIS PROCEDURE if I had been told any this before the surgery. I would never choose a surgery that would have such negative effects on my bladder permanently, especially since a regular hysterectomy could have been done. I would never have chosen this procedure even if this was even a possible risk from this surgical system. I was not told about any risks at all prior to the surgery.

I'm sure that Dr. No had it written in small print on some form or contract he gave me to sign, but I was not made aware of any of them! NONE!

And I don't know if this happens to everyone that gets a hysterectomy performed with this surgical system, but the main nerve to my bladder was cut during the surgery. This made my bladder recovery even harder, and to this day, I have to use all my abdominal muscles to completely empty my bladder. If you don't completely void the bladder of urine, it will most likely result in bladder infections. So I now have to squeeze my abdominal muscles very hard to make sure this doesn't happen. I will have to do this for the rest of my life! Remember, I was only 44 at the time this happened.

After 2 weeks, the doctor removed the catheter but my bladder was still not able to completely void itself of urine. Therefore, Dr. No told me I was going to have to learn how to self-catheter in order to empty my bladder so that I didn't get infections. I, of course, had no clue how to self catheter. I don't know many people that know how to self-catheter themselves. So I had to learn how to do this! Yayyy!

My nurse came into my room and said that she and I had to go into the bathroom so she could demonstrate the inserting of the catheter up into the bladder to allow the urine to drain out. She did all of this to me while I watched her so that I could see how it was done. Let me tell you, this is up at the top of my list of the most humiliating experiences of my life!

I then had to show the nurse that I could insert the catheter properly myself. She made me do this 4 times so that she was sure I could do it correctly. Let me again express how much I would not have chosen this surgery if I had been told anything about these possible side effects. This was like a never ending nightmare! Believe me, no one ever wants to go through this lesson with their nurse! I will say, that you definitely have a closer relationship with your nurse after you experience this together. But, humiliation isn't a strong enough word to explain how I felt, not even close!

For one month straight I had to log how much urine I voided with just using my bladder's ability to empty itself, and then log how much urine I got out by using the catheter. This had to be done about every 3 hours because I had no urge to urinate due to the nerve to the bladder being cut. I wasn't supposed let the bladder get too full because it could cause damage.

The log was measured in cc's or ml. The left column logged the amount of cc's of urine I got out by using my bladder, and the right column logged the cc's I got out by using the catheter. The catheter column definitely had higher cc's at the beginning because of how traumatized my bladder was. But as time went on, the bladder column started pulling ahead and winning this race. Woo hoo! I was definitely rooting for my bladder, of course.

I almost passed out the first time I had to do the catheter by myself when I got home. For some reason it really grossed me out just thinking about the fact that I was sticking this tube up into my bladder. I never worked in any form of the medical field before this time in my life, so it took a little time getting used to doing this. I actually was one of those people who could not stand to watch any medical procedure. I didn't know it at this time, but boy was that about to change. I would have to build a pretty thick skin to medical procedures over the next 7 years.

After a couple of months of doing the "self-cath", my bladder did start working again. Several months after the surgery, other nerves near the bladder started kicking in so that I actually started getting some indication that my bladder was full. To this day, it still takes a lot of effort on my part to make sure my bladder is empty. My bladder was certainly was never like this before before the surgery. I still have to use my abdominal muscles to force the urine out of my bladder to this day.

# CHAPTER 3
# STARTING RADIATION

After 2 months of healing from the surgery, Dr. No's office scheduled me to meet with the radiation doctor. I really did not want to do radiation at all, but I figured it was better than doing chemotherapy and losing my hair.

Looking back and knowing what I know now, and after reading a ton of books on cancer treatments, I believe it probably would have been best if I would have done chemotherapy first to shrink down the tumor. Then, after the tumor was a much smaller size, I could have had a much quicker hysterectomy to remove the cancer. I would have chosen a surgical procedure which would enable the doctor to remove the tumor as quickly as possible, and not keeping me under anesthesia and cut open for 5 hours.

I believe this course of action would have provided much less chance for the cancer to spread. Unfortunately, I had not yet read all the books on treating cancer, and I was still just going along with whatever my oncologist told me to do!

The radiation doctor was a very kind and understanding person and explained all the risks of the radiation and how to to lessen the side effects. He listed and explained the side effects in great detail, which was refreshing. That is a much better doctor in my eyes...someone who gives you as much information as he can and lets you make the decision on your care, after you have all the facts.

The radiation doctor sent me down to see the nurses and I immediately got my 2 little tattoo dots, one on each hip. They looked like 2 little blue freckles. They explained that it had to be permanent marks on my hips because this was how they would line me up everyday when I came in for my radiation treatments. It was kind of funny because I always laughed with my kids and my husband that I was not a cool enough person to ever get a tattoo, and now I could tell them I was "tatted up". My kids actually didn't believe me at first when I told them the dots were permanent. We got a good laugh out of that one because I still don't have any other tattoos to this day.

I started the radiation treatment the following Monday. I went every morning at 7:00 a.m. It took 20 minutes to administer the treatment. My husband went with me to the radiation clinic everyday, of course. He still never misses any appointments because of the infamous hospital incident. Afterwards, we would go straight to work. This went on like this for 5 weeks.

We made lots of friends in the waiting room because we were with them every morning for 5 weeks, going through the same thing. We would all sit and talk before treatment while we had our morning coffee. My husband and I have met some pretty amazing people over the past 7 years of going to treatments and doctor appointments. I am truly thankful that God put all these wonderful people in our lives.

I remember feeling really fine the first 2 weeks of radiation. I actually got kind of over-confident. I was thinking I was going to be unlike all the other radiation patients that had told me they felt so crappy through radiation. Then it hit me! It must have taken my body 2 weeks to start being affected by the radiation, but then the fatigue and loose bowels started. It was really severe. I took about 3 or 4 pills of Imodium AD per day, just so I could just get through a work day. It was unpleasant to say the least. It was quite awful. I think that's sort of implied if you are taking that much anti-diarrhea medication (haha).

I really didn't go many places unless I had to in those 5 weeks. The effects of the radiation may have not started until 2 weeks after I started treatment, but they definitely went on a full 2 weeks after treatment ended. I can remember at the end of the 5th week since starting the radiation, we were invited to go out for dinner with some of our best friends and I had to tell them we couldn't because I was still so sick. I remember crying because I was so upset that I was the cause of us never being able to go out and enjoy life for such a long time. Between healing from the surgery and now the radiation side effects, it had been so long since we were out with other people and actually having a fun with friends, which was something Norm and I really enjoyed doing regularly prior to my diagnosis.

One tradition the clinic had patients do when they finished all their radiation treatments is to ring a really loud bell to celebrate and commemorate your victory. It was a very triumphant feeling! Especially since you feel atrocious most of the time you're doing radiation. I was there for 2 of my friends' bell-ringings. We would bring in doughnuts and celebrate each person's victory. My day of ringing the bell was awesome! We had a really fun time that morning celebrating with our radiation friends. They understood what I was feeling because they were all going through similar situations.

Once I was done with the radiation and had healed up from its effects, I felt so triumphant! I figured this nightmare was finally over! It was November 2011 and I could go back to my normal life because the cancer was gone for good! And that's exactly what I did. At least at that moment. (Let me tell you, Ignorance is Bliss!)

## Checkups & a PET Scan:

I had to go back to see my oncologist approximately every 3 months after I finished my radiation so that he could do a check up and do a pap smear. All was going well for over a year. I then had an appointment in mid January 2013. Dr. No seemed happy with everything, but he thought I should do a PET scan to make sure nothing showed up. I was fine with that and his office scheduled it for the following week.

How a PET Scan works was such an interesting process to me. Here is my dumbed down explanation:
A radioactive atom is applied to glucose (basically sugar) and they injected this into you via IV when you got to the clinic. You then had to lie completely still for about 1.5 hours so that the radioactive material can travel to what is using glucose for energy the fastest. This is why you cannot move. The glucose would go to those working muscles. You're not even allowed to read because the glucose would go to your eye muscles.

So you just lie there not moving. I fell asleep almost right away, so it went fast for me. Ha ha. My husband calls that time travel. When the time was up, they then took me into the room where they do the scan. The machine scans your body looking for the places that light up with the radioactive material.

Cancer is a fast growing cell, so the glucose goes quickly to those cells and lights them up because the radioactive atom is attached to it. Somebody got really rich coming up with that ingenious idea. Boy do I wish it was me!

I received a call the next day at my work from my doctor's office. The nurse actually put the doctor on the phone. Uh oh! That typically is not a good sign. He explained that a couple of spots lit up on my lungs on the PET Scan and he wanted me to get a CT Scan the next day to make sure it was nothing.

I left work the next day at lunch to get the scan at a hospital that was 5 minutes from where I worked. (Incidentally, I had quit working at my husband's company approximately 6 months prior, because he was downsizing due to the economy slump in 2012, so I was working at my brother's practice doing insurance authorizations for his patients.) I went back to work immediately after the CT Scan was done and I was not even worried about the results.

Once the results were uploaded into the hospital computer, I called and had the nurse read me the results over the phone from the radiologist's report, and they were not good. She read the entire report to me. The report stated that there were at least 30 cancer nodules in the right lung and at least 20 cancer nodules in the left lung. The cancer had metastasized to my lungs! How could this be happening? I was supposed to be done with this nightmare forever!

Of course, I called my husband first and he came to my work immediately to pick me up because he didn't want me driving while I was so upset. We spoke to my brother (the surgeon) on the phone immediately, so that he could explain what to expect with a metastatic cancer. He and my husband were very encouraging as always, and I again, was in shock that this was happening because I had convinced myself that I was never going to have to deal with this word "cancer" again.

This day was probably even harder for me than back when I got the call in WalMart, when I was first diagnosed. My first thoughts were again, "I'm going to miss seeing my children getting married." I don't know why this was always my first thought. They were 19 and 21 by this time and were not even seriously dating anyone.

I absolutely DO NOT think this way now, but I was hit with this negative thought: "Well, if everyone in the medical field calls metastatic cancer a death sentence, then why would I even put myself through chemotherapy treatments or any other treatments that will make me sick? If I'm going to die anyway, I'd rather have a good quality of life in the time I had left with my family, rather than be sick with chemotherapy." It was like the nightmare from 1.5 years ago was reoccurring, but only worse.

In the 6 months I had been working at the practice prior to this diagnosis, I had actually spoken to patients that had been diagnosed with other types of metastatic cancer and it always seemed like an awfully grim outlook. So, of course I was thinking that my oncologist was thinking the same about me.

My husband and I went home immediately so we could discuss some of my possible options from what we had read. We prayed and prayed relentlessly that night for God to guide us on what to do and for Him to build up our broken hearts and spirit.

It seemed pretty clear that the oncologist was going to offer one thing… chemotherapy. I had never done chemotherapy, so I really had no idea of what to expect, except that I had heard it makes you nauseated and you lose your hair! Both of those made me NOT want to do it!

But I agreed to go to the oncologist and at least hear him out.

## Letting God Change My Thinking:

We went the next day to his office and he sat and went over what chemotherapies he wanted to put me on. It was an aggressive regimen of 3 different chemotherapies. He did not think the particular trio of chemotherapies he would be administering would make me very nauseated, but he did say I would lose my hair.

I continued praying for God to guide me in this situation because I really did not know what to do. I just kept reading the bible... and God just gave me a sense of peace that I could not explain. My thinking dramatically changed and became so positive and my attitude was completely turned around. I was now just focused on getting better. I know God changed my whole outlook because I was so convinced at the beginning this was a death sentence, and now I did not believe that at all.

My attitude was now: "This Evil Thing Is going to Die by the Power of Jesus Christ!!!"

I was ready to beat this thing with God guiding me.

(I Peter 2:24 KJV), "Who his own self  bare our sins in His own body on the tree, that we, being dead to sins, should live unto righteousness: by whose stripes ye were healed."

I agreed to do the chemo because I really believed I would be that person that would be healed.  My doctor set up my surgery for that Friday to get my port placed in my chest and neck so I could get the chemo without destroying my veins by constantly running IV's.

# CHAPTER 4
# GETTING READY TO START CHEMOTHERAPY

I had to be at the hospital at 6:00 a.m. for the port placement through outpatient surgery. The port placement is a minor surgery, and it went very quickly and easily. I was released to go home by 11:00 a.m. My husband and I were actually able to go out lunch afterward. I was thrilled how much better this went than my last surgery.

I was scheduled to start the chemotherapy the following Thursday. I would now have to miss work every 4th Thursday for treatment. Therefore, I had to sit down with my bosses and change my schedule at work. We changed my schedule to 4 long days so that I could still get in my 40 hours of work. With this change, I could now take Thursdays off. I would go to chemotherapy on Thursdays and then go back to work on Friday.

My chemotherapy nurse told me that I would probably feel fine on Friday (the day after chemotherapy), but that I would probably feel the fatigue and nausea on Saturday and Sunday. She said most people had a delay in the symptom onset. This way I could be home on the days I felt at my worst.

I was a little nervous the first day of chemo, but only because it was a new experience for me. I still had my amazing sense of peace from the Lord, and my husband was with me as always.

I remember walking into the chemo area of the oncologist's office and just taking it all in. There were about 8 recliners, with a regular chair set next each of them. Everyone brought someone with them to keep them company, because I believe they don't let anyone drive after chemotherapy in case of an unlikely adverse reaction. Not that I couldn't drive, but I agree with this safety precaution.

When we would first get there, all 8 patients had to get into a gown and get an X-ray and then an ekg (electrocardiogram) immediately. Then, we would all follow each other downstairs to Dr. No's waiting room, like a little herd, to wait for him to see us. They would call us back, one at a time, and Dr. No would perform a full gynecological exam to get a pap smear. I didn't think anything of it at the time, but I would later go to other oncologists and realized that this was not really a necessary procedure every single time you went for a chemotherapy treatment.

The other oncologists would definitely see you before you went in for treatment to discuss how you were feeling, and to discuss how treatments were going, and then they would do a minor exam. They would listen to your heart and check your blood pressure and get your weight. But no other oncologist that I've seen since then does a full gynecological exam every time you get chemo.

I did not know any of this at the time, but I would find out later other unnecessary things that Dr. No did to just inflate billing to the insurance companies for his own gain. And these were definitely not in the best interest of the patient. This was still the same oncologist that did my surgery and caused permanent damage to my bladder.

After the exam, we would all go back upstairs to the chemotherapy area and the chemotherapy nurse would start us all on our designated chemotherapy treatments, one at a time. So, if you were the last one to see Dr. No and get your exam, then you were probably going to get out of their office about a good 1-2 hours after the first person that saw him because their chemotherapy was started way before yours.

We all had to be there each treatment day at 8 a.m, and we would often not get out of their office until after 5 p.m.. This was an extremely long day, because you spent most of the time just **waiting** for your turn to get the X-ray, or the ekg, or the pap smear exam, or for the nurse to get your chemotherapies started. Dr. No only had one chemotherapy nurse and she was treating approximately 8 patients a day.

I always wondered why there was only one nurse who was allowed to mix the chemotherapy medications and administer them to us. **I would later find out why!**

My first treatment went fine. My husband and I met a really sweet lady named Donna and her friend Deb. We ended up sitting with them just about every treatment day for the next 9 months that I was going to this oncologist for treatment. We were at the clinic for such a long time on treatment day that it was nice to look forward to sitting with people you really liked.

My oncologist told me he was going to keep me on this same three chemotherapies for a full year and that I would go every 4 weeks for treatment. Regrettably, I didn't question it because I was still doing pretty much everything Dr. No told me to do up to this point.

## Saying Goodbye To My Hair:

My chemotherapy nurse told me at the time of my first chemotherapy treatment that I would lose my hair exactly 2 weeks from that day. Based on the types of chemotherapy drugs I was being given, she knew that it would happen at that particular time. She had treated a lot of patients over the years and she was exactly right.

I can remember waking up that day and pulling handfuls of hair out by barely touching my hair. It was crazy. I couldn't believe how accurate she was. I didn't want to spend the entire day watching my hair fall out slowly, so I got my daughter and my granddaughter together in my bathroom and told them I wanted to have them shave it off with an electric razor so that I could get it over with quickly.

Plus, my granddaughter was only 3, so I didn't want her to be afraid of me. If she saw me one day with long blonde hair, and then the next time she saw me I was bald, I thought it might startle her. I was picturing those videos you see on facebook of little kids crying when they see their dad after he shaved a beard and mustache off that he had the child's whole life. The kids would freak out crying because they didn't even recognize their dad. I really wanted to avoid traumatizing my granddaughter like that.

So, my daughter grabbed the electric razor and started buzzing it all off while my granddaughter watched. I was not watching in the mirror. I was just sitting on the floor. Laney did stop at one point so that I could look in the mirror because she had shaved my hair into a mohawk to surprise me. I was cracking up… It was actually pretty cool looking. I kinda liked it! But that would fall out by the end of the day too, so she just finished shaving the whole head. Looking back, we really should have taken a photo of the mohawk before she finished shaving my whole head. When will I ever have that opportunity again.

Losing my hair and having to shave my head was really not one of my favorite days in my life. I was glad I had my daughter there for support, but I don't think many women would look forward to being bald. I've seen women on TV that keep that "bald-look" on purpose, and they really pull it off nicely. But, I was not blessed with the lovely symmetrical head that they have.

I had never seen myself without hair and I really don't think I'm a person that looks good like that. I also distinctly remember how my hair follicles actually hurt while my hair stubble was falling out. It was such an odd feeling. I would touch the top of my head where there was a little bit of stubble left, and it had a very "overly sensitive" feeling. I imagine I'm not the only person out there that has felt this.

I tried not to focus on anything negative and I figured I wasn't going to be bald forever, so I should just keep focussed on getting well!

Incidentally, if anyone is dealing with hair loss from cancer treatments and they don't have enough money to buy a wig, please consider calling the American Cancer Society. My friend got a wig from them during her chemotherapy and gave me their phone number. I called them and those wonderful people had a program in my area that provided me with a free wig. I went to their local office and tried on a bunch of wigs and I left there that day with my new wig (hair). I don't know if that program is going on all around the country, but it wouldn't hurt to call them and check on their local programs. I was thrilled how nice the wig looked on me. That was one less thing to worry about.

I then had to learn how to put on false eyelashes. Everyone getting chemotherapy seems more focused on losing the hair on their head, but we also lose our eyebrows and eyelashes. You also lose the hair on your legs and armpits too. But that part was not that big of a deal to me. You just don't have to shave them for a while.

It's amazing how odd I looked without eyebrows and eyelashes. I went to the store and bought eyelash glue and false eyelashes, and even bought the pre-glued lashes. The pre-glued lashes were an epic fail. I couldn't get those ornery pre-glued lashes to stick. I think I went through the whole package of them with no success.

I moved on to the regular lashes that required me to glue them myself. I would have to get myself psyched up every time I went to put them on. I found it very difficult to get them on straight. I would end up re-doing them 3 or 4 times in an attempt to get them right. Some days I would throw several pairs of lashes out and just start fresh because I was destroying them...it was really frustrating.

Once I finally got them on, I would try and make them last at least 2-3 days. I would be extremely careful when showering to not get them wet and therefore they would last longer. I have absolutely no talent in this area.

I also chose to get my eyebrows tattooed. There was an Aesthetician at the Spa by my work and she was trained on eyebrow tattooing. I didn't have any eyebrows left because of the chemo treatments, and my eyebrow pencil came off very easily. The Aesthetician came to me and offered to do them for free. I couldn't believe it. I was very excited. When I went back to have them done, I was surprised how quickly she finished them and they looked amazing. I couldn't believe how natural they looked. Thanks again Carissa!

I remember it was about 9 months after I started chemotherapy when my hair had finally started to grow back on my head, which was extraordinarily exciting for me. Well, that was pretty much the same exact time the hair on my legs started growing back as well. I know this is going to sound odd, but I was so extremely thankful for hair growth on my head and that I was heading in a positive direction to someday having a full head of hair again, that I began thanking God that I had the privilege of shaving my legs everyday. So, even to this day, (and this has been going on for many years now) I thank God that I get to shave my legs. It is a permanent reminder how blessed I am to have hair on my head. I actually feel privileged to shave my legs. I am certainly a more thankful person now for so many things I completely took for granted before.

**Unexpected Surgery:**

Things seemed to be going along fine with my chemotherapy. I was handling all the different side effects well. I was not missing work, and all my family and friends couldn't be more supportive.

Then, one Wednesday night, my family was at church and I was experiencing a fair amount of discomfort in my abdomen. I just figured I had drank a little too much coffee that day at work, since I drank an extra cup that day.

I told my husband about it while we were listening to the church message. He asked if I wanted to leave, but I didn't want to make a big deal about it. I was already very uncomfortable with all the unnecessary attention I got with all these cancer treatments. I'm not a person that likes to be the center of attention. I'd much rather be in the background.

The next day I woke up and still had pain. Only it was worse. It was my day off work, so I called my husband at his work and told him about it. We were throwing around a bunch of ideas of what the pain could be, and I just figured it was some kind of digestive issue from the chemotherapy and decided to forget about it. My husband called me back a few hours later and asked if I still had the pain? I told him yes and it was a little worse. He now insisted that I go to my PCP and get him to check it. I reluctantly agreed.

I called my PCP's office and told them about the pain and they told me they would make a spot for me toward the end of the day. My daughter was off that day as well, so she went with me to the appointment. We walked into the office an he saw me almost right away. My PCP is probably the nicest person you'll ever meet in your life. He is a super caring person and great doctor. He started pressing on different parts of my abdomen and asking me if it hurt.

None of the places he pushed on hurt at all until he got to the last spot. He pushed on the lower right side of my abdomen and I almost stuck to the ceiling. Woah, did that hurt!

He looked at me and my daughter and said that I was going to have to go get a CT Scan immediately because he was almost positive that my appendix would have to be removed. He knew it was way too late in the day to send me to the clinic that did the CT scans, so he said I would have to go directly to the emergency room to get the CT Scan, and they would probably have to schedule an emergency surgery.

I couldn't believe it. This was really messing up my day off! I had an appointment that day to pick my color for my new eyebrows. So, I went straight from my PCP's office to see the aesthetician who was doing the eyebrow tattoos. I ran in her office and told her that I couldn't stay long because I had to go to the emergency room, but I hurried up and picked my color anyway.

I called my husband **after** I met with her because I knew he would never agree to me going there first. He was definitely not thrilled with that decision. I told him that I was going to stop home and grab a few necessities before heading to the ER. He absolutely disagreed with that idea as well and insisted I go straight to the ER. He called my daughter and asked her if she would bring my clothes and contact solution to the hospital.

I met my husband at the ER and we went in together. They quickly got me registered and showed me to a room. With all of the confusion, I still hadn't had a chance to eat lunch and now it was dinner time. I asked the nurse if I could get something from the cafeteria, to which she said "absolutely not"! She knew that if this was truly appendicitis, and I needed surgery, then my fasting all day ended up being good thing.

I was sent down for a CT Scan right away. The results were exactly what we expected. The appendix was really infected and had to be removed immediately. The ER doctor said he would contact the General Surgeon on-call. It was a few hours later when they took me into surgery. I remember being wheeled into the pre-surgical area and not being nervous at all. In fact, the nurses and I were all actually laughing and joking around. I woke up from surgery and felt fine. The surgeon had done a stellar job and I felt great... but I was still ravenously hungry.

When they brought me up to my room, my family and a few of our closest friends were there. Everyone was eating the food that my daughter had brought from the restaurant where she worked. It just so happened to be across the street from this hospital. It smelled amazing. I again asked the nurse if I was allowed to eat yet, and she said not until the morning. I think that was the most hungry I've ever been in my life. I practically inhaled the breakfast they brought me the next morning.

I saw the doctor later that day and he said I could go home since I was doing so well. We left later that afternoon. I don't think I was even at the hospital for a full 24 hours. It couldn't have gone any better. We even went out for dinner with friends the next evening. Now that's how a surgery should go! Thanks so much to that particular Hospital and their staff (Let's call it Friendly Hospital).

# CHAPTER 5
# CHEMOTHERAPY RESULTS & EFFECTS

I got my first CT Scan since starting chemotherapy after 3 months of treatments.  I can remember calling the nurse and getting the results and finding out that the radiologist's report said that they could **not see any nodules at all**.  Wooohoooo! I think my husband and I called everyone we knew.  I must have thanked God a hundred times that day.  I knew He had been with me during every minute of this whole experience and was comforting and strengthening me.

We were convinced it was gone for good, but my oncologist said I needed to keep going with the chemotherapy because there could still be cancer cells not seen on the CT scan that still needed to be killed.  That made perfect sense to me, so I agreed.

I continued on with the treatment and did 3 more months of chemotherapy and all seemed to be going as planned. However, my side effects from the chemotherapy were getting worse. I had been experiencing several side effects from the chemo drugs. I had extreme fatigue for a week after each treatment. The 2nd and 3rd day after treatment being the worst. The nausea was tolerable, but it lasted about a week, again with the 2nd and 3rd day after treatment being the worst. I had to force myself to eat on those days so that I didn't get too weak.

I also had a nose bleed just about every morning while I was on this chemotherapy regimen. It usually just bled in the morning though. I had a severely raw mouth. Eating anything acidic or spicy was absolutely intolerable. Therefore, my diet became pretty bland. One of my worst side effects was the neuropathy in my feet. My feet were numb and painful at the same time! I know that sounds contradictory, but it is true. I can only explain it by comparing it to when you wake up in the middle of the night with your arm being asleep. Most people have experienced something like this. You've slept on your arm to the point where you have cut off the circulation to it and it's numb; but then it really hurts as the blood starts coming back to it. Well, that's how my neuropathy felt in my feet. I don't know if that's the exact feeling everyone has with their neuropathy, but that is my experience.

At the end of the sixth month of chemotherapy my oncologist sent me for another CT Scan. He said he had to do this because apparently my body does not show much fluctuation in the tumor marker blood count up to this point. Even when the cancer was at its highest amount in my body, the tumor marker count did not elevate extremely high. So, my oncologist had no choice but to get CT Scans to see the size of the tumors and to determine if they were shrinking or growing.

I absolutely hated having to go and get CT Scans every 3 months. I had the CT scan done on my lunch break from work and got the results later that day from the nurse. She read the radiologist's report and it stated that he could again see numerous cancer nodules on both lungs. They had begun to grow back even though I had remained on the chemotherapy regimen.

## Gathering Information:

Needless to say, this was a pretty bad blow. I was doing very aggressive chemotherapies and they were growing back anyway. This was not good at all!!! My first reaction was to immediately start praying. God had gotten me through so much already and He was going to strengthen me through this little setback too.

I believed He wanted me to start educating myself on this horrendous disease and stop just relying on my oncologist for all my information.

There is no evidence that the medical field knows everything about cancer. If they did, there would NOT be so many people fighting cancer in our country, because they would have figured out how to get rid of it by now.

Plus, I believe God wants ALL of us to treat our bodies well... not just those of us fighting cancer. We should do our best to eat right and exercise and take care of the body He gave us. I may never know what is the exact cause of my cancer, but I knew I wanted to do all that I could to kill it, or at least stop or slow the growth of it.

I began to gather books on cancer and I would read as much as I could. This was difficult to fit in to my schedule because of I was so busy between work, and taking care of my family, along with going to and recovering from treatments. I had a really packed schedule during all my years of chemotherapy. I especially liked taking my books to my chemotherapy treatments, because it was probably the only time I wasn't busy with my responsibilities. Additionally, I would try to fit a little reading time into my half hour lunch break at work, and I would read for a few minutes at night after I was done reading the bible. I was usually so whipped by bedtime that I would fall asleep while reading. I would read one page and wake up an hour later with the book on my chest.

## Then the Greatest Thing Happened To Me:

I continued on with the chemotherapy after the 2nd CT Scan results because I figured I had better keep on trying to kill the cancer or at least slow its growth with the chemo drugs. I knew I really didn't have any other real options at the time. I kept on with my research and kept on believing that God had His hand on my life and that He would provide a solution to this somehow. Then I had the best thing happen to me...

I was driving home from the grocery store one Saturday afternoon, just going along with my day as usual. My husband and I wanted to go out and have dinner with friends later that evening, so I had to catch up on tons of cleaning and paperwork if I wanted to squeeze in a little relaxation time. I always did my grocery shopping on the weekends because the weekdays were so ridiculously busy. As I was driving home from the store, like most working moms, I was thinking about the thousands of things I had to do this particular Saturday, when suddenly a statement popped into my brain. (Mind you, I was not praying or listening to the Christian radio station in the car at this time). I don't know how else to describe it!

The statement was, " **This sickness is not unto death, but for the glory of God",**

It just popped into my head. Whoa! I thought to myself, "Where did that come from?" I immediately prayed to God and thanked Him for obviously giving that message to me. It was **NOT an audible sound** at all. But I clearly did not think of it on my own!!

Since that time, I have learned that we all should be sensitive to thoughts and promptings from the Holy Spirit who lives in all Christians' hearts.

I could not wait to get home and tell my husband about this. I ran in the house and didn't even bother bringing in all the bags of groceries. I told him about it and asked him if that statement was in the bible. He said it was so we grabbed my computer and googled the verse. Sure enough, it was part of John 11:4. It was not the entire verse, but I was so thrilled that it was part of a verse in the bible.

God was really making His presence known to me and letting me know that He is in control as long as I trust in Him. I cannot tell you how many times since then, that I reflect on that verse. Every time I get discouraging news from the doctors, I just think back to that verse and I know that God has an awesome plan for my life and that He is going to use me for His glory, **That is the biggest honor of my life!!!!**

I think I have told that story to everyone I know. God works differently in everyone's life. This was just how He worked in mine. He makes every one of us feel special in a different way, because He has uniquely made each of of us!

# CHAPTER 6
# MAKING A BIG CHANGE

I continued to try and get my hands on as much information about cancer as possible even after this because I believe God often works His plan through people. I was also moving along with my chemotherapy every month as recommended by my oncologist.

Dr. No was often not in the office when I would go for chemotherapy treatments because he was an avid hunter. Several times, he was on hunting trips around the world when I would show up for treatment. He was gone so often that he had brought on another oncologist for his practice. That oncologist would perform the pap smear exams when all the patients arrived for chemotherapy and then she would leave while the patients were getting the chemotherapy treatments afterward.

On my ninth month of chemotherapy treatments, my husband and I showed up as usual. Some of our normal friends were not there, so we sat in a different area. We knew most of the women there because we often had treatments on the same days as them. On this particular day, there were probably about 3 patients we just met that day. We all got our X-Rays and EKG's and then went downstairs to the exam floor to take turns getting our pap smear exams. That's when we found out Dr. No was away again.

The woman doctor was very kind and did our exams and we all went back upstairs to start our chemotherapy. For the first 4 hours of being there, everything was going along normally. We were sharing our stories with the new people and just getting to know them.

Then things started getting weird. My one friend started having a severe reaction to her chemotherapy. She had done this chemotherapy many times before, but there is always a chance of a reaction to chemotherapy in a patient's body, even if it's not a new drug to them. I don't know why that happens, but we had been told that many times before.

The chemotherapy nurse ran over and immediately injected BENADRYL® into her IV and then administered the EpiPen® (the Epinephrine Injection). This was scary to watch with anyone, but when it's your friend, it's even worse. The nurse got her back to a normal breathing pattern and she seemed to be recovering.

My husband and I were talking to her and her family and seeing if she was feeling better when, about an hour later, one of the patient's I just met starting having a reaction to a chemotherapy drug that she had done before as well. Again, the nurse rushed over and administered the BENADRYL® into her IV and then followed that with the EpiPen® . But this patient was not responding as well as my friend did. I know she lost consciousness for a while, but I wasn't sure if she stopped breathing. It was really scary to witness. This reaction was so severe that the nurse called the ambulance immediately.

We were right across the street from the hospital, so thankfully the ambulance got there quickly. They came right in and promptly got her on a gurney and brought her to the hospital.

The treatment area was really quiet after that. Everyone was traumatized that this happened twice in one day. My husband and I prayed immediately for the girl that was taken to the hospital. A couple of hours later, my treatment was finished and we left to go home. We talked about how upset the chemo nurse was at the end of this day. She was visibly shaken.

I had never seen anyone have a reaction to chemotherapy before. I was shocked that it happened twice in one day. I felt so bad for both of them. But I just assumed it was one of the risks that we have been told can happen.

That Saturday, I was laying on the couch feeling crappy. I got my treatment on Thursday as usual, so it had been 2 days since my treatment. That's when I always felt the worst. The phone rang and I answered...it was my older brother. He had just received a call from our younger brother who had seen a report on the noon news that my oncologist had been Federally Indicted for bringing illegal chemotherapy into our country and treating his patients with it. My older brother said he would call and break the news to me.

Shock does not even come close to explaining what I felt. It felt like someone kicked me as hard as they could in my gut. You have to understand that as a patient going through chemotherapy, I was not thrilled with how harmful the chemotherapy drugs were to my body anyway, but I figured that I didn't have much of a choice if I wanted to shrink the cancer and live longer. I imagine most people doing chemotherapy feel something similar to that thought.

It's hard enough to accept having harmful chemo drugs pumped into your body, but to learn that Dr. No cared so little for his patients (people that had put their faith and trust in him to help extend their lives) that he was putting their lives at additional risk by giving them drugs that have no regulations or standards of purity on them, it was overwhelming.

In fact, these illegal chemotherapies could have poison put in them for all we knew. Not all countries have regulations on medications. These chemo drugs could have been brought in from anywhere, so who knows what toxins we were being given. I felt so violated!

I couldn't believe that a medical professional that was being trusted to help save lives was actually putting his patients in danger instead. I probably cried harder that day than just about any day through all my years of treatments. That kind of betrayal was hard for me to get my mind around. It was bad enough that this oncologist/surgeon (Dr. No) had performed a surgery on me that I would never have chosen if he had shared with me the proper information and risks that a patient should be told prior getting a particular surgery, but now he was putting me at risk with the illegal chemo that could potentially kill me. Things just never seemed quite right with Dr. No, but now it all made sense.

## Finding a Doctor I Could Trust:

My brother gave me the name of an oncologist he met back when he was a resident and said he was an excellent oncologist. I called that oncologist's office the first thing on Monday to set up a consult, so I could change doctors.

I got an appointment with this doctor within a week. I had all my records sent over to his office. Let's call him Dr. Smart, because his knowledge in this field is amazing. I believe Dr. Smart was the head of gynecological oncology for one of the Friendly Hospitals. He read over all my treatment records and recommended that I get all my upcoming chemotherapy treatments at one of their local cancer center offices. They had a cancer treatment center that was only 15 minutes from my house and he gave me the name of my new oncologist there. I was so relieved. It was like a weight had been lifted off me.

I showed up for my first treatment and met my new oncologist. Let's call him Dr. Kind. He talked to me for a quite a while about my symptoms and side effects of the previous chemotherapies. We discussed all my options and which chemotherapies he thought I should be getting now. He is a wonderful oncologist and a very caring person. I couldn't believe the difference in having a doctor that actually cared.

After the exam he sent me out to start my chemotherapy. The staff of nurses that administered all the chemotherapy were very kind and professional at my new cancer center. I was amazed at the how different the atmosphere was here at the Friendly Cancer Center compared to the secretive and unusual procedures that I had witnessed at Dr. No's oncology office.

It made sense now as to why the old oncologist's office had only one chemotherapy nurse and why she was the only one that was allowed to mix all the chemotherapies for every patient. They were obviously hiding a BIG SECRET. Namely, that they were not using not FDA approved chemotherapies. I was very thankful that I was not receiving treatment there anymore and that God had led us to this new group.

I completed my first year of chemotherapy in January of 2014, since I had started treatments in February of 2013. My oncologist sent me for a CT Scan at the end of January, and unfortunately the results showed that the cancer had grown again. He recommended a new chemotherapy regimen and I agreed with him. I wanted to take a month off though to let my body have a break, and he reluctantly agreed.

## Seeking New Treatments:

Through my first year of reading books and researching any possible natural remedy for cancer, I started to discover dietary changes I could implement that claimed they could at least slow the growth of the cancer. This made sense to me. I figured that even if it didn't work, I would at least be eating really healthy, which is always a good thing.

I also began to read information on clinics around the country, or around the world, which were claiming they were having success healing people from cancer. One clinic in particular was in Texas. I read the book that was written about this particular doctor who came up with this treatment and figured it was worth a phone call. I called and inquired about their treatments and they emailed me a ton of information. They did not claim they could cure everyone, but listed the success stories they had.

I told the woman I spoke to on the phone that I wanted to set up a consult, and she said I would have to pay $1200 up front. I told her I would have to speak to my husband and call her back. All of the other people/clinics that I had read about that were claiming success stories seemed a little harder for me to believe. That's the crazy thing about having this disease-- you want to believe everyone who is claiming success. But, it's really expensive to pay for these alternative programs because they are not covered by insurance. Therefore, you basically have to pick the one that sounds the most believable. I'm not saying that any of them are lying, but I couldn't afford to go see them all. If I had more money, I probably would have tried every one of these treatments because I was determined to beat this thing.

At the same time I was reading all these books, my husband and brother had been researching clinical trials for which I might have qualified. Clinical trials look for specific patients -- with specific cancers -- and who have completed specific treatments -- and who are at different stages of cancer. There are so many qualifications, I could never list them all here. Which is why it is so difficult to be selected for them. My husband found a specific trial online that was going to be done at a respected hospital in Maryland. He emailed the information to my brother to get his medical opinion on it. He also believed it was worth the time to check it out.

I seemed to have all the qualifications that were listed, so I contacted their office and asked if I could be considered for the trial. The receptionist was very nice and asked me several questions on the phone and then immediately emailed me a list of forms I had to fill out and fax back to them. She also sent a list of records I needed to send them from the hospital where my original surgery was performed. I completed everything in record time because I was so excited that I could possibly be a part of a promising new treatment.

After about a week, I again contacted the office that was in charge of conducting this clinical trial, and spoke to the same woman. She said they had received everything I had sent them, and that I should come in for an interview with the doctor who was in charge of this trial. She set up the interview for the following week.

That night my husband and I also discussed the clinic in Texas and decided it was worth checking it out as well. My husband and I also shared all the information with our family because we really wanted those closest to us to us hear the evidence and make sure we all thought it was worth the money. Everyone unanimously agreed they were both worth a shot. I called the next day and paid the $1200 on a credit card and made the appointment for the clinic in Texas. The trip really didn't cost us anything beyond that because we thankfully had enough points on our credit card to pay for the flight and my mom graciously let us use her saved points for the hotel. I was feeling really optimistic about everything because I had 2 appointments set up with totally opposite types of treatments and figured that one of them had to work out.

The first appointment was with the oncologist at the hospital in Maryland regarding the clinical trial. The hospital was 4 hours away from us, so my husband and I both had to take a vacation day from work. I was so excited that I didn't even care. I was constantly hearing about new innovative treatments for cancer on the news. I thought this could be a great way to get in on the new treatments before they became available to the general public. We were both so excited and had such a positive attitude the entire ride there.

I can remember that morning in February very clearly. We left Pittsburgh on one of the most frigid days of the year. The outside temperature was well below zero. We didn't even care. I remember arriving at the hospital and filling out additional paperwork and waiting for quite a long time. When we finally went back to see the oncologist, we went directly to her office, not an exam room. Let's call her "Dr. Arm".

Dr. Arm immediately started asking me questions about which trial I was there to talk to her about. I was confused and thought to myself that she should have known that information since I had sent them such a large amount of my clinical information. After all, they had set me up for a consult with her for that specific clinical trial.

I told her the name of the particular clinical trial that I had come to discuss. She had a very rude and very angry tone immediately. Dr. Arm replied in a disgusted tone that I didn't qualify for that trial because I had already done chemotherapy. She said that fact alone disqualified me. But, she said she had another clinical trial that I should do instead. It was not a trial that sounded like it would be very effective for my type of cancer, so we declined her recommendation and again asked about the study we had been scheduled to discuss.

She acted annoyed that we were not interested in the clinical trial she wanted me to do. I questioned her as to why her department set me up for a consult for a specific clinical trial if they knew I did not qualify. Wouldn't the professionals who pre-qualify patients clearly see that I had already done chemotherapy on all the information I had faxed. I had sent a plethora of clinical information. They should have told me that I was ineligible instead of wasting our time and getting our hopes up if that was the case.

She was *really* getting annoyed with us now!

Dr. Arm then blurted out, "You've only got a year to live since you've got metastatic cancer!"
I replied, "I've already lived a year with metastatic cancer".
Then she said, "You may have been lucky so far, but this is going to kill you!"

This was downright unprofessional. I was appalled at how I was being treated.

I couldn't believe that this well-known hospital had set me up for a consult for a clinical trial that I didn't even qualify for, and also that we had just driven 4 hours to go there be treated so callously. And quite frankly, I can't imagine a person who seemed downright hateful would even be working in a field like oncology. Human kindness is something that we should all try and express to one another no matter what field of work we are in, but especially when you are interacting with patients who are dealing with life and death matters.

My husband was livid. He told me later that he never stopped watching my face the entire time we were in Dr. Arm's office. He said that if he had seen one tear in my eye, he was going to tell this "so-called" medical professional off. I personally stopped listening to her as soon as she uttered those negative and hateful words. Norm went ahead and took the forms Dr. Arm handed him regarding the clinical trial she was pushing very hard for me to do, and then we said goodbye.

We left the useless consult and went straight to the elevators. As soon as the elevator doors closed, I looked at my husband and said, "Wow, wasn't she a peach!" We got a good laugh about that one. That appointment had turned out dramatically differently than I had hoped. I still believe to this day that God put a shield of protection up for me in that office to protect my emotions. Normally if someone spoke to me with such a hateful attitude regarding such important life and death issues, it would have made me really upset. But on this day, I wasn't affected by her at all. I knew God was in control and I didn't have to listen to this seemingly angry and callous person.

This is an important note: We all need to rebuke lies spoken to us from anyone. God's Word says He wants us well. Anything contrary to that is a lie.

We got back in the car and headed home. I wasn't thrilled that we both wasted a vacation day for that "negativity fiasco", in addition to all the money wasted on gas and eating out for all three meals that day, but it certainly seemed clear that this was not the direction God was leading us. We had plenty of time to talk about it on the 4 hour drive home, but we were still encouraged that we were scheduled the following week for the clinic in Texas. Hopefully there would be better news there.

The following Thursday evening, we left for Texas. We made the consult for Friday morning so we only had to take one vacation day for this consult and we only had to stay one night at the hotel. We arrived late Thursday night and went straight to the hotel. Our consult was early in the morning so we had to get a little sleep.

The next morning we arrived at the building and were very impressed. It was a big, beautiful building owned by the doctor who came up with this new medication. We waited only about a 20 minutes and then they took us back. We met with the doctor (let's call him Dr. Z) who had developed the medication and 3 other doctors that worked for him. They all read over my clinical information that I had faxed to them. They saw that the cancer was metastatic to my lungs and that I had already completed a year of chemotherapy. They spoke of other patients they had treated with similar types of cancer and how they responded to their treatment.

They gave us an overview of what they would do for me, which included chemotherapy plus their own innovative treatment. We also went over some dates available, so I could get and idea of how soon they could start treatment. My husband and I said we would take all the information home with us and discuss it with our family and get back to them as soon as possible.

We left the consult and had to head straight to the airport to leave that afternoon because we had made the return flight for the same day as the consult. We were determined that we didn't want to have to stay another night and incur any additional expenses. We read over the information numerous times and talked about how we hadn't really found any other clinics or treatments that were having as much success as this one. Not to mention, we had such a better experience with these people than with Dr. Arm at the hospital in Maryland.

When we got home we discussed everything with our entire family and presented all the information we had been given. They agreed that this option was worth trying.

We were going to have to get a loan to pay for the treatments since they required all payments be made up front. They even made you pay for insurance covered chemotherapy medication up front. They said that they would submit all chemotherapy treatments to our insurance company, and reimburse us as soon as they got payment from the insurance company. However, we would be completely responsible for paying for their innovative medication because it was not covered by any insurance.

I had insurance coverage through my work, plus I was also still covered on my husband's family plan, so I figured that we would probably get complete reimbursement for the chemotherapy since I had such good coverage. Once reimbursed, we could pay some of the loan back. Until then, we could just make minimum payments until we got reimbursed. The cost of the other medication would just have to be something we would make payments on for quite a while in hopes that it worked.

# CHAPTER 7
## TRYING AN ALTERNATIVE TREATMENT

We called the clinic in Texas the following week and set up an appointment to start treatment the first week of March 2014. I would have to stay in Texas for 2 weeks while getting my treatment.

In the meantime, I had to go see my new oncologist, Dr. Kind and discuss how I was going to try this experimental treatment. He was very understanding about why we were trying something new, but expressed that he was not a proponent of this new treatment and he didn't think it was very promising. I told him I definitely wanted to continue treatment with him as soon as I got back. He was fine with everything but thought that we were wasting our money going there in the first place.

We left the first week of March and stayed in Texas for almost 2 weeks. It was a long time to be off work for both of us. Fortunately, my husband was able to get much of his work done online. I couldn't imagine how much of my work would be piled up for me when I returned, which really worried me. Also, there was still the nagging feeling this medication might not work.

On the bright side, my Mom still had a ton of points left on her credit card which paid for our hotel the entire time we were there, so we just had to pay for our flights.

We arrived in Texas on a Sunday night and started treatment early Monday morning. We were at the clinic all day getting exams and bloodwork and chemotherapy. **But something had CHANGED** since we had spoken to them at the consult the month before. The innovative cancer treatment medication the doctor had developed that was working so well on killing cancer cells in so many of their patients -- and was pretty much the entire reason we went there -- was now not allowed to be administered! **What???**

They went on to explain that the FDA had put regulations on their organization so that they could no longer administer that medication. Instead, they had a pill that they could give me that they believed would react in a similar manner in my body as the other medication and hopefully have the same effect. That's right...hopefully!

This sounded odd to me and my husband. Something seemed really wrong about the whole thing! But, I had put so much of my hope into this medication that I was now just hoping they were right at this point. So, we agreed to try it anyway.

When you are in a situation that seems like you don't have many options and you feel like your back is against the wall, (like we were in) you often make excuses for things that don't really make sense to you because you desperately want to believe they are true.

We probably should have known that without the innovative medication that I went there to get, and the fact that they could no longer could legally administer it, **we should have left right then!** Instead, we stayed and they administered 3 different chemotherapies and I started taking the pills that they said would replace the innovative medication that made them famous.

Looking back with 20/20 hindsight, my oncologist at home could have been giving me the same chemotherapies, and I could have taken their pills at home that were their "substitute" for the their innovative medication. But since we had invested so much in this, we stayed the whole 2 weeks, desperately hoping our suspicions were wrong.

They were all very nice people and we did enjoy the time in Texas. It is a beautiful state. I can see why there is such a large population of people in Texas, because it really seems like a wonderful place to live.

When my treatments were finished at their clinic, I can remember how excited I was to just go to the airport after being gone for so long. I had never been away from my children or my granddaughter for such an extended time period. Plus, I was really bummed out that I had missed my daughter's birthday. I had never missed any important day for my kids or grandchild. This really bothered me!

## Heading Home:

We had planned to take our daughter and the family out to dinner on the day we got home to celebrate her 21st birthday. Our flight was supposed to arrive in Pittsburgh around 11 a.m. on that Saturday, which would give us plenty of time to get home and unpack all our clothes and still leave plenty of time to go out to celebrate.

We arrived at the airport at 5 a.m. that Saturday morning and went through security and got to our gate with no problems. We had plenty of time to eat breakfast. Since our flight was scheduled to take off at 7 a.m., we sat and waited for quite a long time. It was now 7:30 a.m. My husband and I were really starting to wonder why this flight was running so late. Finally, they announced that it would be delayed for a full hour. After that hour passed, they announced it would be delayed another hour. Much later, they eventually announced that the airplane was having mechanical issues and they were sending for another airplane from another airport.

Apparently, the mechanical issues were so extensive that it would take too long to repair. We were on our computers the next minute looking for another flight, but it would have cost us at least an additional $500, because this airline was definitely not going to give us our money back. Don't you just love airlines sometimes!

We were really in no financial position to be spending another dime. We had already spent so much on this trip, especially with the loan we had to take out to pay for treatment and the money we had already paid for the flight. The airline gave each passenger a whopping $7 to spend on food while we waited. Let me tell you, $7 is not much in food vouchers when you are waiting 18.5 hours at an airport!

We ended up being at the airport from 5 a.m. that Saturday morning until 11:30 p.m. that Saturday night. We finally boarded the plane and I believe we took off before midnight. We got into Pittsburgh around 2:30 AM on Sunday. We had been up since 4:00 a.m. the day before, so we were exhausted. And worst of all, we missed our daughter's birthday dinner. I felt like such a bad mom. I hated missing her birthday, but then missing her birthday dinner celebration on top of that was killing me. I actually felt selfish for even going for treatment in Texas at this point.

Once we got home, it was such a joyful reunion with our family. I had such high hopes that this pill that I was taking 3 times a day would actually work. I went back to my oncologist a few weeks later and he continued me on the same chemotherapies they were giving me while in Texas. I told him about the pills they had given me and his opinion was that he still did not believe they were reputable. I was hoping he was wrong.

**More Chemotherapy:**

After three more months of chemotherapy, my oncologist sent me for my CT Scan to check the size of my cancer nodules in my lungs. When I went to see him for the results, he showed me the scan and read the radiologist's report that showed the nodules had shrunk a little. I was elated to hear this after doing more chemotherapy, which had made me lose my hair a second time. Again, I don't think any woman I know is happy about going bald. But, I had just begun to grow hair back from the first long stint of chemotherapy and I certainly hated to see that hair fall out again. The hats get annoying after a while and the wigs make your head so hot in the summer that I could not stand to be out in the sun with them on. I absolutely love summer and I really enjoy sunshine and being outside, but now I couldn't go outside or go to work without wearing a hat, scarf or wig . Although the wigs looked nice, no one previously told me how itchy and uncomfortable they were. I scratched my head constantly.

Despite being uncomfortable, I always wore the wig to work because when I wore scarfs, it was really obvious to others I was doing cancer treatments. It became too time consuming to answer all the questions about my cancer treatments to every concerned patient that came through our office. Although I greatly appreciated how caring everyone was that asked how I was doing, it became exhausting to explain the story so many times a day. We had so many kind and wonderful patients, and I certainly didn't want to make them feel badly. I worked at a very busy office and I had a ton of work to complete by the end of each workday, so I tried to not let people know what was going on.

One extremely embarrassing moment with a patient and her husband was the final straw with me wearing scarves to work. I was sitting at my desk in the common area at my work which included multiple desks that were all connected. It was set up as a large open work area so that if the employee who sat at the front window walked away for a moment, there would be plenty of co-workers to back her up and service our patients that came to the office window. My desk was actually the furthest away from the patient check-in window, but because it was one big open area, everyone could hear the conversations going on at the window with the patients.

One morning, a particular patient had brought her husband with her to her appointment. He was standing at the patient window with his wife while she was checking out, and he was being kind of loud and was joking around with my co-worker at the window. He suddenly blurts out, "Hey I see you have Brett Michaels working here with you today", while he was pointing at me. And then he let out a big laugh because he thought he was hilarious.

My co-workers politely did a slight smile so they wouldn't offend him, but knew this was such a rude remark about a person who obviously was just wearing a scarf on her head because she was trying to cover up her bald head from chemotherapy. I sat there stone faced the entire time. I could not believe someone would say something so insulting to a person going through an already difficult situation. I held it together as best I could until they left and then I ran to the ladies room and cried my eyes out. (In case you don't know who Brett Michaels is: He is the lead singer from the band "Poison". He always wears scarves or bandanas on his head. I believe it's the style that he is known for now).

How on earth could a person think that it was funny to mock someone who is battling something this difficult and who is already hurting? I really don't understand it to this day. But, then again, I know other cancer patients who have had people say the most thoughtless things to them as well. You wouldn't believe some things fellow-patients have told me regarding things people have said to them.

**A Few Don'ts:**

Just as a heads up to people who have a friend or relative going through a battle with cancer, here are a few **Don'ts.**

1. Don't give them negative statistics you have read that are going to bring them down. I'm sure they've already heard them all.
2. Don't tell them about other people who have lost their battle with cancer. They need to hear all about other people who have won their battle!

3. You don't have to believe every word that comes out of your doctor's mouth. I've already listed a few examples of doctors that were not positive people and said very discouraging things to me. Again, not every doctor is good at what they do.

4. Seek out doctors that are going to have the same positive mindset as you.

We need to stay 100% positive and keep an  attitude of unwavering faith that we are going to beat this cancer!  Do not accept negativity from anyone!

# CHAPTER 8

# FINISHING THE 2ND YEAR OF CHEMO

---

I finished out my chemotherapy in 2014 at my oncologist's office in June, and continued on the pill regimen from the clinic in Texas until October 2014. By the time my oncologist sent me to get my CT Scan in October 2014, I had been off of chemotherapy for 3 full months. I went to his office to get the results, and he read the radiologist's report like always.

He informed me that the cancer nodules had grown in the 3 months since I had been off of chemotherapy. Even though I had continued taking the pill regimen from the Texas clinic in that 3 month period, the cancer nodules had still grown. It was painfully obvious now that I had been paying for this pill regimen and taking them religiously and they weren't doing a thing to shrink the cancer. It was also apparent that all the shrinking of the cancer nodules that we saw on the previous CT scan had been from the chemotherapy. It's not a great feeling when you find out you've been paying thousands of dollars for a "medication" that **did NOT do one thing to help you.**

I was very disappointed with this substitution medication this clinic had given me. I called their clinic and told them I would not be ordering any more of their pill regimen and I would like to be contacted as soon as they received payment for the chemotherapy treatments from the insurance company. I wanted to at least be reimbursed for the chemotherapy treatment, which was covered by insurance. I was starting to be annoyed that they made me pay for the chemotherapy up front since I knew it was covered by the insurance. They told me I would be contacted as soon as they received payment.

I know that insurance companies are not lightning fast at paying a doctor's office for treatments, but I at least expected I would hear from them by the 6 month point, which had already past. They said not to worry, they should receive payment soon.

The Texas clinic had submitted my chemotherapy treatments to my insurance company for payment, but they could not submit the pill regimen to insurance company because it was not eligible for coverage through any insurance. This means I paid for this "medication" for 6 months that did absolutely nothing. I do believe that if I had gotten to this Texas clinic before they were banned from treating people with their original medication, it might have worked, but this pill regimen was probably an inferior replacement for their original treatment. This substitute treatment was certainly not working on me.

My husband and I discussed it and figured it was time to move on in our research since this was an obvious dead-end. We had learned a lot from this failed experience and we would definitely try to not be so gullible with the next steps in our research. Talk about a painfully expensive lesson, financially and emotionally.

## Obtaining a New Biopsy:

Toward the end of 2014, we were at a regular consult with my oncologist. He was a very dedicated and thorough doctor, and he was always researching any new medications that had been approved for treatment. At this particular consult, we were discussing the cancer that was in my lungs. He asked me if my previous oncologist ever actually obtained a biopsy of the cancer in my lungs to verify if it was metastatic cancer from my original cervical/uterine cancer, or if it was a second type of cancer altogether. He said the previous oncologist probably just assumed it was metastatic cancer? I told him that no biopsy was ever done.

He believed this was something that was worth checking on because it would change the types of chemotherapy he was giving me if it turned out to be lung cancer instead. He immediately had his medical team get an authorization for a biopsy to be performed.

I went to the hospital a week later for the CT Guided Biopsy. I had never had this procedure done before, so I had no idea what to expect. We arrived at the hospital very early in the morning and the staff got me prepped very quickly. They took me into the room where it would be performed and the doctor explained that he was going to insert a needle through my skin, muscle and then through my lung. Once he was in the lung, he would take a sample of one of the cancer nodules. I had to stay perfectly still. You really didn't want to mess up such a precise procedure. Fortunately, it all went extremely well.

The next day I returned to work. I had no pain and felt fine, so I figured why miss work? But then as the day went on I started to feel short of breath. It was the oddest feeling. I was talking to patients on the phone and calling insurance companies like always, and I could barely speak. I was so short on air that speaking was becoming almost impossible. I had no idea what was going on. So, I went in to one of the exam rooms at work and laid down for a few minutes to try and get my breathing to return to normal. This was not helping.

I went into my younger brother's office and told him that I was going to leave because I didn't feel well because I was really short of breath. He told me I should go to the doctor to get it checked out since I had just had the biopsy the day before. I told him not to worry and I would be fine. As I was walking out to my car, just by chance, my older brother had come down to our office after surgery and my younger brother told him that I was short of breath and I was going home. He came sprinting out of the building and caught me before I left. He questioned my symptoms and told me I was possibly experiencing the start of a pneumothorax and I needed to get to the hospital immediately to get it checked. I told him I just wanted to go home and I would be fine. He very emphatically told me (in other words: yelled at me) that I was going to the hospital. He explained that if my lung completely collapsed I could die. I wasn't aware of that.

I agreed to go to the hospital but I wanted to drive myself there. He wouldn't let me do that either since my breathing was becoming more and more labored every minute. He knew that if I got into a traffic jam on the main roads going to the hospital, it could take at least an hour to get there. It was Friday in Pittsburgh, so traffic was a guarantee, so he called the ambulance. I was so embarrassed as my entire office of co-workers watched me be wheeled out. But, it ended up being a good thing. By the time the ambulance reached the hospital, I was literally gasping for air.

I remember seeing my son as they were taking me out of the ambulance. I was so happy to see him, but I felt so badly that he had to see me gasping so terribly for air. I hated putting my family through all this constantly. My husband got there right after him, followed by one of the pastors from our church. I was talking to all of them when the ER nurse came in to access my port. The nurse said everyone had to leave the room so he could access the port in a sterile environment.

Right before everyone left the room, my pastor prayed that God would repair the lung. They all walked out and the nurse got a port needle that looked entirely too large for my port, but I didn't say anything. He stabbed it into my chest area with an **extreme** amount of force and completely missed the port. Wow, that hurt! He tried it a second time with the same result. I was amazed at how hard he was pressing the needle into my chest, not to mention that he was completely missing the port.

I told him how much he was hurting me and asked if someone else could access my port. I had my port accessed hundreds of times for chemotherapy over the past couple of years and it never hurt like this. It was usually just a little pinch. He left the room and my husband came in. I whispered to him that this nurse was really hurting me and I didn't think he knew how to access a port. As I was talking to him, my husband suddenly said, "Hey, you can breathe again!"

He was right. My gasping for air had completely stopped after this guy stuck the needle in my chest. We never saw that nurse again after he left the room. I still think about that day. It just amazes me that this guy came and went so quickly and I was suddenly okay --- and we had just prayed for God to repair the leak. My husband is convinced that the nurse was an angel. I think that is a definite possibility, but if not, then God sent the right employee to my room to accidentally relieve the pressure, because he definitely wasn't accessing the port.

About a week later, I returned to Dr. Kind's office to discuss my results. He said the biopsy confirmed that the cancer was metastatic from my cervical/uterine cancer and not a new type of cancer. This was useful information for my oncologist, but not really great news for me because that meant the cancer was more difficult to eliminate from the body because it was definitely Stage 4 metastatic cancer.

## Continuing the Research:

My husband and I were determined to not let this news get us down and we started out 2015 determined to find a new treatment that was having success. I had completed 2 years of chemotherapy by this point and it had begun to take a toll on my body. We had been hearing and reading a lot about stem cell treatments for various medical treatments, so we thought this would be something worth researching further. We actually had met a doctor that my brother knew who was involved in a stem cell clinical trial for "fat grafting."

I started communicating with him via email and he was keeping me updated on his research. He was not sure if stem cell treatments could be used for cancer treatment but he wanted to do some research on the subject and he would keep me posted. My communications with him were inconsistent over the next 6 months of 2015. I had been telling my long-suffering oncologist about this new doctor and his stem cell experience, and my oncologist stated that he was not aware of any study or trial where stem cell treatments were being directly used for treating cancer in the U.S. He wanted me to be careful since he had told me something similar about the last failed treatment I did in Texas.

I knew he was right. So I kept trying to contact this doctor for the the next month. He finally responded to my emails that he was not sure he could do anything for me at this time. Again, I was disappointed.

Most people probably would have said I was searching for something that was never going to happen, but I wasn't going to give up. I don't think God wants us to ever give up. He is with me everyday and strengthening me in every situation, so even if I don't find the right answer right now, I will eventually find the right answer with perseverance.

(Galatians 6:9 KJV) And let us not be weary in well doing: for in due season we shall reap, if we faint not.

## A Life-Changing Trip:

At the beginning of 2015, my husband and I were surprised with a gift from two of our closest friends. Our amazing friends were going on a trip to Israel and surprised us with 2 tickets to join their group tour. We were blown away. This was a trip that we had wanted to take for years but my medical expenses had depleted our savings.

We were there for 10 days and went to a minimum of three different biblically historic sites each day. We were rebaptized in the Jordan River; we toured Jerusalem and Bethlehem; we went to the Western Wall;  we visited Calvary and we stood inside the tomb where Jesus' body was lain.  We went in the the Dead Sea; we visited Jericho; we saw where the Dead Sea Scrolls were found; and we visited some caves where David hid from King Saul.  The list could go on and on.  Visiting Israel really brings the Bible to life like nothing else.  I actually took notes while we were there because there was so much to learn.  We had a great guide as well a pastor who was extremely knowledgeable about the history of Israel, which was very important.  I would recommend this trip to anyone!  It was incredible.

# CHAPTER 9
## PRAYING FOR HEALING

---

At this time in my treatment, my husband became very serious about researching healing in the bible. It was something that we had never really learned about at any of the churches we had ever attended. I grew up going to a Catholic Church and then switched to a Non-Denominational Church in High School. My husband had never really attended church growing up. My husband and I began our marriage going to the same Non-Denominational Church my family had attended for several years. We later found a Baptist Church that we really enjoyed about 19 years after we were married.

All of these churches we attended were great places of worship and I believe that we were supposed be at each of these churches during the time we attended them. They all taught us about what it means to be a Christian. They each taught that Jesus Christ is the Son of God and that He came to this earth in order to die on the Cross to pay the price for our sins, and then He was raised on the third day to fulfill the Scriptures! And, if we believe on Jesus Christ as our Savior, we will receive our salvation and be with Him in heaven at the end of this life. Our salvation is a wonderful gift from Jesus our Savior that clearly illustrates the Grace of God. I believed on Jesus as my Savior at a young age and I have always been thankful for my salvation and God's guiding hand in my life.

Although all the churches I attended were wonderful places of worship, we had never really learned an in depth amount about healing at any of them. We had read about all the people Jesus had healed in the bible, and all the people that His disciples and other apostles had healed as well. But we were never really taught specifically about how to pray for healing. I am very grateful that my husband was so motivated to research the bible about healing at this time. He is a very intelligent person and retains information better than most people, and he was very motivated to learn about healing because of me. He continued in his research over the next few years.

We began to pray constantly that God would cast this evil cancer out of my body. My husband was still at the beginning of his research, but we know God desires all of his children to be well. We didn't really know what to expect, except that we knew God had given me that verse. (John 11:4) A few weeks after we started our praying, I was home one day by myself and all of a sudden started coughing and coughing and finally brought up a good sized bloody ball from my lungs. I spit it into the sink so I could take a look at it. I called my oncologist's office to see what he thought about that. He was worried, and he didn't want to take any chances, so he sent me to the emergency room to make sure I didn't have a blood clot. I told him I didn't think it was anything like that, but he was concerned, which I appreciated, so I went.

My husband came home from a meeting and we left immediately. We waited for what seemed like forever at the ER. When the doctor finally came in, he also wanted to make sure what I coughed up wasn't a blood clot, so he sent me for a test. Everything came back normal, and there were no clots. This was good news, but what had I coughed up? Two days later I coughed up another blob of tissue, except this time there was hardly any blood and a lot more white/tan colored substance. Again, I had spit it in the sink so I could show my husband. He and I started to wonder if this was dead cancer. We had been praying for the cancer to be cast out, and we thought it was literally being cast out.

We believed that it was. Over the next six months I continued to cough these blobs (for lack of a better word) out periodically. It was not all the time, but it sure resembled what you would think that dead cancer cells would look like.

Could it be? I'll tell you the results later.


## Continuing the Search for Clinical Trial:

We decided it was time to move on **again** with research. We had been reading about immunotherapy trials since I was diagnosed with metastatic cancer back in 2013, but there were never any trials for which I was qualified because they were not conducting them for people with my type of cancer. I had never even submitted my information to be considered for an immunotherapy trial up to this point because you had to meet **all the criteria** for that particular trial or they won't even consider you. I had never found any immunotherapy clinical trial that was for my specific type of cancer.

We continued to search any hospital in the country who was conducting clinical trials for immunotherapy that was opening it up to a more varied group of cancer types. We finally got the name of a doctor in California by the end December 2015 that was conducting a larger amount of clinical trials involving immunotherapy. We were told to contact his office and see if they were doing any studies where the the trial was not specific to a particular type of cancer, so that way I could be considered.

We called the office immediately and they made an appointment for us in February 2016. We had to set up a flight to California immediately. This re-energized us. At least we had hope for a new treatment. Again, we were faced with more expense, but we knew God would provide. We told our family about this consult and everyone was really excited about the possibility. Our church, as always, was praying for us. We started going to our church back in 2009 and knew how blessed we were to have such a supportive church family that was always in prayer for us. This time was no exception. Our pastor actually surprised us and told us he was cashing in his points and giving them to us to pay for our flights. We were so relieved, because now we only had to pay for the hotel for 1 night since we were going to come home right away.

It was very important that we didn't spend too much money because we still hadn't received our reimbursement from the clinic in Texas. They had promised they would pay us back for the chemotherapy treatments as soon as they were paid from the Insurance Companies. It was now February 2016 and they still had not paid us back from 2014. I knew they had been paid because I had received the "Explanation of Benefits" from the Insurance Companies and I saw exactly how much they had been paid. I kept on calling their clinic and no one would ever call me back. When I would ask the receptionist why their financial people would not call me back, she would just say she didn't know and would put me through to the voicemail of a different person each time. This had been going on for a long time now and it didn't seem like I was getting anywhere. My husband and I were just about ready to consider legal help at this point.

## Off to California:

At this time, we were not really thinking about those negative things going on with the Texas Clinic because we were very focused on staying positive about the potential of this new immunotherapy treatment. We were hoping it could really be a viable option for someone like me that was dealing with metastatic cancer for 3 years now. I wanted to remain positive. I remember leaving our house for the airport at 2:30 a.m. on that February morning. I didn't even care that we got no sleep. I was way too excited to sleep. Our flight took off by 5:30 a.m., and with the time change, I believe we got in to California at around 7:30 a.m.. It was awesome! Our appointment for the consult wasn't until 3:00 p.m., so we had all day to see the sights. It was such a relief to be in a warm climate for a day when it was so cold back in Pittsburgh. The temperature in Pittsburgh in February is usually the coldest of the whole year, so we were loving it that we got to walk around all day without coats on and feeling the sun's warmth on our faces. Most people that live in the NorthEast **really** appreciate warm weather, especially in February.

We arrived at the cancer clinic at 2:30 p.m. and waited to see the doctor. Once we were in the exam room, the Physicians Assistant came in first and asked me a slew of medical questions and we went over all my clinical information I had faxed to them a few weeks before that detailed all my previous treatments. After the P.A. finished all the questions, the doctor came in and we quickly went over the same information so that we were all up to speed on the what type of cancer I had and all the chemotherapies, radiation & surgeries done up to this point. He told us specifically about 2 different trials that were coming up that were **not** specific for a particular cancer type, but were developed more for people with various types of stage 4 cancers. That was me, since all cancer that is metastatic is considered stage 4. He thought these would be the best 2 trials to consider, and he was going send me down to the lab to get specific blood work done that was required for each. He said that once he received all the results for the blood work, he would contact me and inform me which trial he would recommend. He said it would be several weeks before we heard from him.

We left the consult absolutely elated. This was the most positive and most hopeful doctor visit we had ever had since the time we thought the chemotherapy had eliminated all the cancer back in 2013. We went back to the hotel and had dinner and fell asleep immediately after dinner since we had not really slept the night before. No wonder we passed out.

We got up early the next morning and left for the airport. I wanted to get back to work right away since we went for the consult on my day off. We went home and told the whole family how great everything went and they were just as hopeful as we were. We waited patiently for the rest of February and the first half of March. I was so hopeful to hear from the doctor. Unable to wait any longer, I finally called their office in Mid March 2016 and they told me that the doctor had been trying to contact me. I think he might have had the wrong email address or I had his email wrong. No matter though, because once we got the contact information fixed, he sent me information about the one immunotherapy trial that he had recommended. He also informed us that this trial had amazingly just opened up in the Pittsburgh area. I was blown away. This couldn't be more perfect. God always comes through for me!

I was amazed! The trial that the doctor thought would be a very viable option for me was actually opening up in 3 other cities in the country and one of them was Pittsburgh.

It's awesome to be one of God's children! He gave me the name and phone numbers of the 2 doctors that were doing the consults to qualify the patients for the trial. I called immediately and was set up for both consults for the same day at the end of March 2016.

I remember being so hopeful that morning. I thought that this could be the medication that would work on killing the cancer. We walked in to the office of the first doctor, and as always, I answered a massive number of questions. We were the first patients of the day, so we went back to the exam room in no time. The doctor came in and started questioning me about all my previous treatments and my whole cancer history and why I wanted to be considered for the trial. When he starting talking about the trial, he couldn't hide the fact that he did not want me to do the trial. He was a doctor that specializes in a specific field, and I could tell he wanted to save those spots in the trial for his patients. I explained the extent of the chemotherapy that I had already tried and how I thought it was time to try something that might work better and not have such negative effects on my body. He said that he believed I should just stay on the chemotherapy regimen.

I was crushed! We left the consult and went straight to a restaurant to eat breakfast since we had 3 hours to kill before the next consult, so there was no sense driving home. I wish I had a video of my face during that breakfast. I was incapable of creating a smile. It was like someone was trying to suck the air out of my hope balloon. I barely even said a word. I was heartbroken. There's no way to even describe the sick feeling in my stomach.

My husband tried to encourage me by reminding me that we still had another consult to go that day, but I can clearly remember the severity of my discouragement. It's not a good place to be. Discouragement is lethal. This is why all cancer patients need a good support system of family and friends. Things will happen in every cancer patient's battle that will try to bring them down, or they will get discouraging news, or some negative person will say a hateful thing. We need those loving and supportive people in our lives to remind us to not believe those negative things or negative people.
We need to be reminded of:

(Romans 8:28 KJV) "And we know that all things work together for good to them that love God, to them who are the called according to his purpose."

Boy, did I need to hear that. We went to the second consult and waited for a really long time. The doctor had just come back to work from an injury and she was really struggling physically. I personally couldn't believe she was even there. I felt very badly for her because she was obviously in pain. She is an amazing oncologist. She read over all the treatments I had done previously and listened to the reasons why I believed that this would be a good time to try something different as far as a treatment that could have better results for attacking the cancer, without all the side effects like chemotherapy (or at least less side effects.)

This doctor agreed with me and said that if it was her, she would be ready to do the same thing. I can't even tell you the relief that washed over me. I'm sure she had no idea how much her words meant to me! I wanted to cry with happiness. As horrendous the last doctor made me feel, this one had completely encouraged me!

The oncologist said she would have her team start getting the paperwork ready and would have them set me up to come back in for a final consult in a few weeks to sign everything that would allow me to participate in the clinical trial, and I could get all the required blood work drawn at that time as well. Additionally, I would need to get a CT Scan to establish the size of the cancer nodules at the start of the clinical trial. We went home that afternoon and we couldn't stop sending out group texts to the family and close friends about how exciting this opportunity was. We had a completely new energy. What a dramatic difference from my morning appointment.

I started the new clinical trial in April 2016. The staff at the Cancer Center, where the trial was being conducted, was awesome. They were such a caring and encouraging group. They were also a "Friendly" facility. I can't rave enough about their care for their patients. We went for treatments exactly as the trial required and they monitored me very closely. It was a very interesting process. I believe I received treatment for around 2 months before I got another CT Scan to see if the immunotherapy was working. I went back for my next treatment after the CT Scan and the oncologist came in and read the results of the radiologist report. The cancer nodules had grown. The oncologist told me not be discouraged yet because the immunotherapy often takes a while to kick in and start seeing the results, which gave me more hope.

I stayed positive and continued on with the treatments. I was really enjoying being off of chemotherapy. Three years was a long time have chemotherapy be your only "go to" treatment, and I really felt like my body needed that break. I believe it was a couple of months later when I was sent for another CT Scan. I showed up the day of immunotherapy treatment like always, which was about a week after the CT scan. The oncologist came in and read me the radiologist's report and she explained how the cancer nodules had grown once again. That wasn't even the bad news though. What was worse was that in order for me to remain on the clinical trial, the cancer nodule growth had to be below a specific size, and **I did not meet that criteria**.

We actually had to leave the clinic that day right after meeting with the oncologist. She had no control over that, because she had to follow the requirements of the clinical trial. She genuinely seemed to feel really bad for me that I no longer qualified to receive treatment, but it was part of the protocol requirements of the trial. It was no one's fault...my body just didn't respond to that particular type of immunotherapy.

This oncologist was always very encouraging, and she recommended other immunotherapy trials that were possibly coming to Pittsburgh in the next year. She told me that she was moving away and taking a position in another state, and she would not be there any longer to guide me to another trial, but that I should keep in touch with Barb, the clinical trial coordinator, over the next year, who could guide me to any new clinical trials for which I may qualify.

There were several other types of immunotherapies being developed at that time and I figured I could try another in the future. This technology was advancing so quickly that I was still very encouraged. I even started seeing commercials on TV for certain immunotherapies...none of which were approved for my type of cancer yet though. I vowed I would not let this get me down. Things were changing in the field of cancer treatment. I could see it.

# CHAPTER 10
# BACK ON CHEMOTHERAPY, AGAIN

---

I was not going to let this one setback test my resolve. The next week I was back at my oncologists office. Dr. Kind was happy that I had tried the immunotherapy and he was very encouraging as always. He said we would start on a chemotherapy right away to try and reduce the size of the cancer nodules which had grown significantly larger, which he did. I started chemo that day, after I received an echocardiogram to make sure my heart was still healthy enough to tolerate the chemotherapies that he was planning to administer. My oncologist was concerned about that because I had done so much chemotherapy already that he wanted to ensure I had not sustained any heart damage.

He sent us over to another clinic to get the echocardiogram. We were sitting in the waiting room when I started to cough and brought up another cancer nodule (blob). This time I was prepared. I had been keeping a specimen bottle in my purse so that when I coughed up another blob, I could capture it and bring it to my oncologist to send it out for a biopsy. When we went back to my oncologist's office, I showed him the specimen.

I asked if we could send the specimen out to pathology. He was kind of laughing because I had been telling him about these blobs that I had been coughing up periodically for a while now. He had told me it was almost impossible that I was actually coughing up cancer. We also have a few friends that are physicians that also told us they did not believe it was probable that the cancer was being coughed up. So, our belief that it was actually the cancer being expelled by my body, was unlikely.

But, my oncologist was such an open-minded professional that he believed we should check out all possibilities, and he sent the specimen to pathology anyways. He was still emphasizing to us to not get our hopes up that the cancer was being coughed up, and that we were probably wrong. I think he was trying to protect me from disappointment. He said it all very nicely though, and then sent me down for the chemotherapy treatment.

Three weeks later I went back to Dr. Kind's office for my consult with him and to receive my next chemotherapy treatment. We were sitting in his office when his P.A. came in and showed us the pathology report about the specimen we had sent out (one of the blobs). She was very excited to show me that it had come back as positive for my specific type of cancer. It was identified as adenocarcinoma, which is the exact type of cancer that I have always been diagnosed as having. My oncologist came in after we read the report and we all got a good laugh about it. He was still shocked, but was happy for me that some of the cancer was literally leaving my body. It was very encouraging news since I was definitely not thrilled that I had to go back on chemotherapy, again.

As I had let everyone know, I was pretty bummed out that I had to go back on chemotherapy again. This was now my fourth year since being diagnosed with metastatic cancer. I had started 2016 doing chemotherapy, and then had a break from it by doing the immunotherapy trial, but I was now going to finish the last 6 months of the year with chemotherapy. This particular chemotherapy regimen that I was on, was making me extremely sick!!! The nausea was much more severe than any other chemotherapy I had ever done.

I would always do the chemotherapy treatments on Thursdays. I had made this my day off at work at the very beginning of doing chemotherapy years before because I was usually feeling pretty decent the first day after chemo treatments, and then I would experience my more severe symptoms, such as extreme fatigue and headaches, on Saturday and Sunday. This enable me to be home for my really bad days, and then I would be able to function by Monday and go back to work. But now, with this new chemotherapy regimen, every time I got a treatment, I could barely make it through the workday on Friday because of the severe nausea.

I would feel terrible all day at work, and then I would rush home to just lie down and not move. The nausea would start very quickly. The nausea was so intense the entire weekend that I could not even get out of bed except to pee. I would run in to the bathroom as fast as I could and then sprint back to bed. If I laid **perfectly still**, it definitely lessened the intensity of the nausea and I could keep from throwing up. If I moved around at all, I would throw up. I tried every anti-nausea medication and home remedy that had ever been invented, but nothing seemed to work.

I don't know about other people, but when I was really nauseated, I could not read the written word. You would think it would be a good time to catch up on books you've been wanting to read, but I couldn't do it. I could listen to audio books or audio readings of the bible on the app on my phone, but I could not read any written book because it required me to focus my eyes, which inevitably made me more nauseated. It was awful!

I have to admit that I actually started to develop an intense fear of going to the chemotherapy treatments. Just knowing I had to look forward to those 3 days of not being able to move at all and feeling so horrendous, made me sick to even think about. Those days of laying there were very emotional for me. I felt absolutely useless! It was like I was completely missing out on life. I can remember crying more on those days than any other days throughout this long journey. I had never felt so helpless. Any time my children or my husband would come up to my bedroom to see me, it was very difficult for me to keep from crying, because I felt like I was missing out on sharing in their lives.

Imagine feeling absolutely horrendous for 1 week out of every 3 weeks in your life. I don't know how to accurately describe it except to say that the chemotherapy was stealing away a large amount of my quality of life with my family and friends, which made me incredibly heartbroken.

I have always been an extremely active person. From the moment I woke up until I finally sat down at night with my husband, I usually didn't sit still much except to be at my computer at work. I went back to work when my kids were very young, so I wasn't used to being sedentary. I was also very conscious of staying in shape and working out, in addition performing all of my "mom and grandma" responsibilities. It didn't leave much idle time in my life.

I had done so many years of chemotherapy prior to this and had dealt with a variety of side effects, but I always considered the nausea as the worst side effect (besides baldness). All of the other chemotherapies invoked a much milder nausea. The other chemotherapies certainly did not make me hungry, but the nausea was tolerable and I could function quite normally. This new chemotherapy regimen made me throw up for days. Even when the nausea symptoms became less severe, by approximately Monday, I still had no real desire to eat for several more days. It took a whole week before I would feel back to normal with my appetite.

Here is a tiny example of how awful the nausea was. My favorite drink in the world is coffee! To me, it is seriously delicious! I would probably drink it all day if I thought that was healthy. I typically only allow myself 2 cups a day, so that I don't get carried away with it. I drink one cup in the morning so I can feel alive, and then one cup in the afternoon as a treat. But, when I would get this chemotherapy treatment, I could not even look at coffee or smell it until a full week after doing the chemo treatment. I could drink nothing but water for a full week. Everything was disgusting to me. I force-fed myself food so that I could attempt to stay healthy. Additionally, I believed that keeping a little bit of food in my stomach helped to tone down the nausea.

It seemed like every year I did chemotherapy, the symptoms would get more and more intensified. I don't know if all those chemicals build up in your body or not, but it definitely felt like it to me. I finished 2016 doing chemotherapy.

Every time I went to the cancer center for my chemotherapy treatment, the nurses would give me a medication that helped your body produce white blood cells after the treatment was completed, which is very helpful to patients struggling to keep their white count up. The nurse would attach a small medication box to my arm after treatment, and it would administer the medication automatically the next day.

This small box had a thin needle that was inserted into your arm, and was programmed to start administering the medication at a specific time the next day. Once the box completed the administration of the medication, the light would "go out" on the box, and then I could remove it.

It was a great idea and a good medication. But, because I had to go for these chemotherapy treatments every 3 weeks for such a long period of time, and I would always begin to be sick the morning after treatment, I had started to associate my nausea with this medication box. I know logically that this box of medication had nothing to do with making me nauseated, but because it was still attached to me when I started feeling atrocious, my brain associated it with the terrible nausea. So, to this day...every time I see a commercial for that medication on TV, I instantly feel sick to my stomach. I feel like a Pavlovian dog with their commercials. I still have to sprint to grab the remote control and change the channel. Just talking about it now is making me nauseated. Aren't our brains funny?

By the end of December 2016, I had become so tired of feeling sick all the time, and my body had become so beat-up from doing chemotherapy for the last 4 years, that I was ready to be done with chemotherapy forever. I told my husband and my children how discouraged I had become due to how abused and horrendous my body felt all the time. It was probably the lowest point in all the years of fighting that I experienced. So, I finally admitted to them that I did **not want to do any more chemotherapy**.

It just didn't seem to be shrinking the cancer enough to justify continuing the treatments and destroying my body. I remember the day my daughter walked into my bedroom to talk with me since I was right in the middle of the "sick days" after chemo where I couldn't move or I'd throw up. To this day I still can't come up with the appropriate words to describe the depth of how atrocious I felt. I literally felt like a shell of a person physically. My daughter would come in periodically to cheer me up in between my naps. She was so compassionate and encouraging that I will forever be grateful to her and my whole family for getting me through that time.

I choked through tears to tell her that I just didn't want to do chemotherapy anymore because this was no way to live. My quality of life had reached an all time low. She completely understood and reassured me that she was not angry about it at all. But then she gave me the surprise of my life.

For her entire life, I had been begging her to let me be in the delivery room when she had a baby someday. She would always laugh and tell me that was gross. But I always persisted that she was my baby girl and I would be honored if she let me be there. So, on this day she told me that even though I was going to stop the chemotherapy, she wanted me to keep on fighting as hard as I could to beat this thing because she was going to let me be in the delivery room one day when she had a baby. I couldn't believe it! I was so happy I started crying again. As if I hadn't cried enough that day. But this time they were tears of joy. Now, mind you, she was only 23 years old and had just started dating her new boyfriend, so I didn't think this was happening any time soon. Fast forward to 6 months later and those 2 got engaged, and fast forward to Fall 2017 and they got married. Fast forward to Spring 2018 and I was in the delivery room to watch my beautiful daughter give birth to my precious granddaughter. My daughter loves to imitate me in the delivery room crying while I told the hospital staff, "I got to see my baby girl have her baby girl".

My daughter is very funny and everyone cracks up when she tells the story. I kind of like it too because it's a reminder to how blessed I am that God allowed me to be there. Thank you Jesus!

Looking back now, I think God had been waiting for me to to completely trust in Him for a long time. I certainly didn't want my family to think I was giving up, but I was just going to focus on seeking out alternative treatments and putting everything in God's hands. He had given me the verse, John 11:4, four years before, and I was just going to trust that God would work this out. He must have given me this verse for a reason. I just had to have faith that He would work this out.

My family and I had previously researched a lot of new treatments and supplements and had tried as many of them as possible. I wanted to keep that open mindset and pursue any new or potentially effective treatment that was available, but it was definitely time to close the door on chemo.

## A quick "Thank you":

On a side note, I do have to give a quick shout-out to the people of the TV show "Pit Bulls and Parolees". I discovered this show in my many post-chemotherapy days of sickness and nausea where all I could do was watch TV and not move. I was desperate to distract my mind on how sick I felt. I would DVR every show of "Pit Bulls and Parolees", which had apparently been on for many years. I had actually never heard of the show until 2016. So I made sure we recorded every episode. It didn't matter if they were re-runs or new episodes. I didn't care because I hadn't seen any of the shows. I believe, in the approximately six months of doing this particular chemotherapy, I watched just about every episode ever recorded over the last 7 or so years that the show had been running. I was so inspired by the kindness and compassion of these people that were rescuing animals that had been abandoned, abused, lost or had been used in dog fighting. They were also giving jobs to men that had just been released from prison and needed an opportunity for a new start. They were actually making such a difference in so many people's lives. It was very inspirational to me because I really love animals, especially dogs. Tia, her family, and her workers unknowingly helped me through a very tough time. I couldn't tell this story and not share what a great group of people I think they are.

I encourage all cancer patients to find something that inspires you and takes your mind off what you're enduring. It truly helps a lot. As I've stated, it was impossible for me to read when I was nauseated because reading would intensify the nausea, so I would listen to my audio bible app on my phone or audiobooks or watch "Pit Bulls and Parolees". I needed these things to take my mind off of the debilitating nausea.

## Constant Coughing:

It was also around the end of 2016 that I began to get chronic pneumonia. My first bout with pneumonia was in October 2016. I had been coughing and coughing for the entire month. I just figured that I was having trouble getting rid of a cold because of the amount of chemotherapy I had done that had affected my immune system. But, looking back now, the fact that some of the cancer nodules had grown together and become one very large tumor was surely the major reason I couldn't stop coughing. The tumors were affecting my lungs' ability to do its job. The one tumor was now taking up the entire left lower lobe of my lungs. I believe the tumors were not allowing my lungs to work properly and get rid of bacteria naturally.

I finally went and got an X-ray after work one day. The X-Ray Technician called my oncologist immediately after getting the results because it looked so bad to him. My oncologist called me that night and put me on antibiotics immediately. I took the entire course of antibiotics thinking that would take care of the cough. By December 2016, I was coughing just as badly and went back to get another X-Ray. It confirmed that I had pneumonia again.

I was disgusted, because it had become really difficult to work. I coughed all day long. My co-workers thought I was sick constantly and the patients thought I was going to infect them. Even when I knew I didn't have a cold, people automatically assumed that I did. By January, my cough had become so bad that I would often go into coughing fits that would make me throw up. I guess the body (lung) knows there is a foreign object in there and is trying to eliminate it.

I was coughing and coughing to the point that I couldn't even speak. I could barely get through a sentence on the phone with patients without coughing in their ear. I knew I had to go back for another X-Ray. Just as I thought, it showed the pneumonia was back again. I couldn't believe how badly my lungs were working. The cancer nodules had really started to affect me functioning in public.

I chewed mint gum constantly. I would have to get a new piece every 20 minutes or so to help keep the coughing fits from getting out of control. Chewing this much gum really upsets my stomach, but I really didn't have much of a choice if I wanted to be able to lessen the amount of coughing fits and be able to actually finish a sentence.

I had never realized how much people stare at you when you cough until I acquired a chronic cough. Most people feel compelled to comment on your cough too. Complete strangers constantly stared at me and they often felt the need to say something. Some people would ask if I had a bad cold, while others asked if I had asthma. Some people just asked if I was alright. Many people offered me a cough drop or gum. Others would just stare or walk away so they don't catch what you have.

I certainly didn't want to make anyone feel badly, so I usually just said "thank you" and agreed with whatever they said. I think it would probably make people feel badly if I said the truth, "No thank you, I actually have a massive tumor in my lung and your cough drop really won't help" (LOL). That would be horrendous to do to strangers that are just trying to be nice! But, I really hated the attention I was getting from all the coughing. I found myself going out less and less.

# CHAPTER 11
## A NEW YEAR WITH HIGH HOPES

Dr. Kind ordered another CT Scan for me in January of 2017. It had been at least 3 months since my last scan and he wanted to see if the chemotherapy was working. He had me come to his office to go over the results. He read the radiologist's report and it showed that the cancer nodules had grown quite a bit even while on chemotherapy. This was not good! It was a clear indication that my body stopped responding to the chemotherapy. He started to go over some options with my husband and I. One of the options involved an FDA approved immunotherapy that was becoming more widely used. This was a completely different kind of immunotherapy than what I had done during the clinical trial the year before. This immunotherapy had not been specifically approved for my type of cancer with the insurance company, but my oncologist thought the insurance company may approve it if we proved that the chemotherapies were not an option for me anymore because they had ceased to work.

Dr. Kind was going to get his staff to work on getting an authorization right away. He set me up for another consult with him 2 weeks from that day and we would discuss if my Insurance Company had approved that immunotherapy at that time. If they did, then I could start the treatment immediately.

I went to my consult two weeks later, and my oncologist explained that his staff had submitted a ton of clinical information to my insurance company regarding all the different chemotherapies that had been administered to me over the past 4 years, and had submitted the most recent undesirable results of my CT Scan. The insurance company could see we had exhausted all the chemotherapy options and they approved the immunotherapy drug for me! He was very happy that we could get started immediately. He did not want to waste any time because the cancer nodules had grown together into such a large tumor that he was really getting worried, and didn't want me to go another day without some type of treatment. So, I went into the clinic area and got the first treatment immediately. I again have to reiterate what a caring and diligent oncologist I was blessed to have.

I received three months of this treatment and then my oncologist ordered the CT Scan as usual to see if the immunotherapy was being effective at shrinking the cancer, or at least stopping the growth. I returned to my oncologist's office a week after the Scan to get the results. Dr. Kind showed me the scan and read the radiologist's report. All the cancer had grown! The number of cancer nodules had actually become less because I had coughed so many of them out, but the remaining cancer had become quite large. He could clearly see why I coughed so much and got chronic lung infections.

My oncologist informed us that he was not sure if this immunotherapy was ever going to work on my type of cancer. It was a newly approved treatment and he had read only one report of this immunotherapy being administered to someone with my type of cancer, and it had not been effective. He did add that some immunotherapy effects are delayed in shrinking the cancer, but he also had no guarantee for me. He asked me if I wanted to continue on with that treatment? I said "yes" because I was hoping that it would eventually work.

I continued to receive those immunotherapy treatments for 3 additional months. After the 3 months, I had to get another Scan to track if it was being effective at killing the cancer. The following week, we were back at my oncologist's office to have him read the results. He seemed to be a little discouraged when he walked in the room. He read the radiologist's report that detailed how the cancer had grown even more. He told me that it was obvious that the immunotherapy was not working on me because the results of the medication would have kicked in by now if it was going to be effective on my type of cancer. He showed me the size of the really large tumor. It was basically the size of a softball. I couldn't believe how huge it had gotten.

Dr. Kind was extremely concerned about my breathing because of the size of that tumor. He knew the difficulty I was already having with my breathing and the extent of the coughing and pneumonia. He told me he was out of options. He didn't have anything else in his arsenal for me to try at this time. He sounded very defeated to me. I felt badly for him because he had always been so encouraging and kind in all my years with him. It must be an awful feeling to tell a patient that there is nothing more you can do to help them. He will always be one of my favorite people. What an amazing and caring person!

Dr. Kind then informed that he could send me back down to the oncologist that had originally referred me to him. That oncologist, Dr. Smart, was at a different "Friendly" Facility and they handled a lot of innovative and new treatments that were being tested in clinical trials. He promised to email Dr. Smart immediately.

My husband and I thought that was a great idea, and he set up my appointment right away. Before I left his office, I reassured him that I was going to be fine and not to worry because God was handling this and I was going to be healed.

## We Really Needed Some Good News:

Dr. Smart was the same oncologist I had seen 3 years prior that had referred me to Dr. Kind. He is also an excellent oncologist and a very caring person. He seemed to have a ton of responsibilities in his position, but he still takes time with each patient, so you can tell he truly wants the best for you. He sat down with Norm and I and told us about 2 separate clinical trials in particular that he thought would work for me.

The one trial was extremely innovative and little harder on the body than the other clinical trial, so each patient had to be very healthy besides having Stage 4 cancer. Quite a difficult requirement. But hey, that was me! Also, the people heading up the trial **just so happened to be looking for someone with my type of cancer at that particular time! I knew God had this thing under control! That was no coincidence for sure!**

I told him I would like to apply for that specific trial. He said he would submit all my clinical information to the trial group and schedule me to come back within a week to register for it if I was accepted. Or, we would talk about getting me into another trial, in the event I was rejected.

The day of my appointment the following week, I was anxiously waiting and hoping I had been accepted when Dr. Smart came into the exam room. He went on to gladly report that I had been accepted into the clinical trial. He said he previously wasn't sure if I would get accepted because my type of cancer was an Adenocarcinoma, which is odd for a cervical cancer, but he was happy they accepted me in spite of that fact. An innovative research company had been developing this technology/process for 20 years. Then he started to list the stages involved in the trial. **It was not just a new medication. There was way more involved**.

He told me I would have to undergo a surgery first, in order to retrieve a biopsy of my cancer. The biopsy had to be a particular size to meet the requirements of the trial. Therefore, someone from this Company had to be present at the surgery to retrieve the biopsy properly and preserve it in accordance with the trial and then return it to their lab. The Company would then take the cancer material and basically grow a new immune system for my specific cancer in their lab (Rest assured, that is an extremely dumbed down explanation because I'm sure I wouldn't understand their scientific terms. I am sending out a heartfelt sorry to all the doctors and scientists that are aware of how much more is involved in this actual process).

Then, after several weeks of healing from the surgery, I would be admitted into the hospital, where they would begin this process by administering chemotherapies to me that were originally developed for leukemia patients. These chemotherapies would basically wipe out my current immune system. I believe this was to get rid of the old immune system that did not recognize my cancer as a bad thing, and therefore was not doing its job to kill it.

The doctors would continually monitor my cell counts, and once they were where they wanted them to be, they would then administer the "new and improved" immune system they had grown in their lab, which would now recognize this evil cancer in my body as a bad thing, and would now attack and kill it!! Woohoo!

I still can't get over how smart these people are! I was blown away that this could even be done, let alone that I was blessed enough to be chosen to participate in it. This was so very exciting to my husband and I. I knew it was going to be a long, tough process, but I could easily see that this was the most ingenious ideas I had ever heard regarding fighting cancer, and I didn't want to miss out on its benefits. Thank you Jesus for bringing these awesome people into my life!

Dr. Smart's office scheduled me with the thoracic surgeon immediately. This practice of surgeons was also part of the "Friendly" Health System, which I was so thankful for since switching my care over to them several years before. My husband and I went to the consult with a very optimistic attitude. I knew how blessed I was to have such tremendous care. The surgeon came into the exam room and we discussed my latest CT Scan and the surgical options.

The surgeon explained which tumor he was going to remove. He chose a smaller one because he said he could not just take part of the very large tumor that I wanted him to remove. I wasn't aware of that. I was kind of hoping to get rid of the largest one. He said that it was taking up most of the left lower lobe of the lung. Whoa! It had really grown!

The surgeon chose a surgery date with us and they had me sign all of the required paperwork and we left. We had scheduled the surgery for only a week later. I was elated that this was going to happen so fast. I just wanted to get this process moving since everyone was telling me how serious everything had become with the now enormous size of the one tumor. I went home and received a call not long after I got there. It was the nurse from my new surgeon's office. She told me the date that we had picked for the surgery was not going to work for the people at the Research Company because they were going to be in another state that day. I completely understood that they were very busy people. The earliest day they had open was a date that my surgeon was going to be out of town. So they picked another day for my surgery that worked for both of them.

My surgery was now going to be about a month and a half from the day of my initial consult with my surgeon. I almost fell over. I was so disappointed. I asked her if there was any other date they gave as an option? She said she would call them back first thing in the morning and ask them for any other possible dates that would work for their schedule and my surgeon's schedule.

I was really hoping they could move this surgery up. She called me back the next morning and told me she had discussed it with my surgeon and he had okayed another date that also worked for them. The surgery was now only going to be approximately 3 weeks from that morning. That was such a huge relief. I thanked her for taking care of this and I told her how much I appreciated it. I didn't want to give the cancer too much additional time to grow.

I tried to use that 3 week time period wisely because I had been planning my daughter's wedding all year. She had gotten engaged in January 2017 and the wedding was in November 2017. Any mom who has ever planned their daughter's wedding knows that most of the responsibility falls on the mother of the bride. Also, I didn't want her shower or wedding to suffer just because her mom was dealing with this crap. I wanted it to be as perfect as possible.

I had never planned a wedding before so I was kind of "flying by the seat of my pants." Also, I had to throw the wedding shower the third week August, and my surgery was the first week of August. Yikes. There was so much to get done before I went into the hospital for surgery. And, since I had no idea how good I would feel after surgery, I wanted to have everything completely done and all food ordered, before I even went in for the surgery. On the bright side, my daughter was a dream to plan a wedding for. I would call her constantly and tell her the things I had done or was planning to do, and she always had the same reaction, "I love it".

We seemed to be on the same page as far as her style for the reception, plus she was incredibly appreciative of everything I was doing. I don't think I have ever heard of anyone so relaxed about their wedding. She figured that as long as they ended up married at the end of the wedding day, they hit their goal. Because of how easy-going she was, I got everything completed for the shower and was making great strides in getting things done for the wedding well before my surgery.

## Surgery Day, Again:

The day of the surgery finally came and I was so very ready for it. I wasn't nervous at all. I just really wanted to get the process started that would kick this cancer's butt. My husband and I had to be there by 6 a.m. and they got me admitted immediately. I went back to get my IV started and to be prepped for surgery. Everyone was great at the "Friendly" hospital. After they put me under anesthesia, I don't remember anything of course until I was back in the recovery room.

When I woke up, I didn't feel hardly any pain, but I was groggy. I immediately asked for my glasses like always. Again, I am so very blind without my glasses or contacts that I have asked for them immediately after every surgery. They had my husband bring them back to me right away.

With each surgery I had during these last six years, I never stopped getting excited to see my husband once I woke up from surgery. He is my absolute rock every day of my life and through every experience I have been through.

The nurse then brought me up to my room at the hospital. The nurse made sure no one was allowed into the room until they transferred me into the bed. Since you're not wearing anything under the gown, I wanted to make sure all my private parts were covered before my family came into the room so I wouldn't traumatize my poor son.

I was disappointed that my granddaughter was not allowed to come to the hospital area where I was sent after surgery. That was kind of a bummer. But maybe it wouldn't have been good for her to see me hooked up to so many tubes. She was already 7 years old and was the light of all our lives since she was born.

When the nurse finally let everyone in to my room, it was awesome because I got to see both my kids and their fiancés (because they were both engaged at this point.) And they had let in my mom and dad with my husband. The surgery had gone perfectly. My family had all been worried because I had never had a surgery like this before. They remembered what happened with the lung biopsy. That pneumothorax certainly wasn't anyone's fault, it just happens sometimes. We all sat and talked for a quite a while. Eventually, they all said I needed to rest, so they all left for home.

I still had my husband with me as always. Thank God! I always felt like things would turn out fine as long as he was there. He, of course, stayed the night. He looked so terribly uncomfortable in the recliner that was in the room. Plus, he uses a BiPap machine every night of his life at home which he didn't have with him. So, he was trying desperately to not fall asleep for fear he would wake up the whole floor with his snoring. We had a nice evening together at the hospital and I was feeling great, so we were thankful that God had sent us to this surgeon and to this hospital.

The next day, the surgeon came in first thing in the morning and told me he needed to check my chest tube. I was feeling fine, so I asked him if it would be ok if I went home. He said as long as he took the chest tube out I would be able to go home later that day. That was exciting news! He and his Physicians Assistant told me they were going to take the chest tube out and I had to lean on my left side. I was extremely nervous that it would hurt, but they did it so lightning fast that I barely felt it. That was a huge relief. I was so impressed. I actually went home later that day and rested.

# CHAPTER 12
# STARTING THE BIG PART OF THE TRIAL

---

I received a phone call from the Clinical Trial Coordinator about 2 weeks after I was home from surgery. She told me that the Trial contact had not given her the exact date that I would be admitted yet. They were still growing my new immune system in their lab. These T-Cells (white blood cells) in your immune system, are generated from stem cells in your bone marrow. (I'm still not completely sure how this all works in our bodies, so I'm simply explaining my understanding of it. I am certainly not a doctor.) I believe it takes a different amount of time with each type of cancer to grow the specific amount of Lymphocytes needed to successfully carry out the study.

She explained that it would probably be around 6 weeks after the surgery that the    Trial personnel would have everything ready and I would be admitted.   She also told me that I would probably have to stay in the hospital for around 3 weeks once admitted to complete everything required for the trial. I was floored. I couldn't believe that I was going to have to be away from my family that long. I knew they could come and visit me occasionally, but it was not going to be often because the hospital was almost an hour away from where all of my family lives, unless there was absolutely no traffic, which almost never happens in Pittsburgh.

Everyone in my family is very busy during the weekdays with work. Because I am so close with my family, this news was upsetting. I asked if there was any way to make my stay a little shorter, but she said it would be very unlikely because they have parameters set for the clinical trial. My blood work would have to meet certain criteria before they would release me to go home.

I was determined that I was going to be that one patient that was going to be released out of there early. The Trial Coordinator called me a week later and gave me the date that I would be admitted. This was very exciting. It was finally sinking in that this was going to happen. My date was September 12, 2017. So, I went into overdrive with wedding plans. I got a serious amount of wedding planning done in that six weeks between the surgery and the day I was admitted into the hospital for the trial. That made me feel very relieved before going into the hospital. I knew about 75% of my part was done, but I still had to pay a several vendors their final payments, but everyone else had been paid in full and all was booked.  Phew!

## A Long Stay in the Hospital:

On the day of my admission, I had a serious pit in my stomach.  I was just sick that I had to be away from my family for 3 weeks, plus I figured I was going to feel pretty lousy while I was here.  I remember walking in to my room that was going to be my home for the next 3 weeks and feeling like the day I would be released was **so extremely far away**.  It felt like an eternity.

I knew this trial was going to be tough on my body and I figured I was going to get really sick with the chemotherapy.  Having this all ahead of me was not making me feel very good this first day.  Doesn't it always seem like the first day is the most ominous when you are starting something new?

I have to say that the staff at the "Friendly" hospital where I was admitted made that first day a lot easier.  They were all very kind and encouraging, and they explained everything they were going to do to me in detail before they did it, so that I would be more comfortable.  Having the right people take care of you makes all the difference in the world!  I encourage every person I have ever spoken to about their health care practitioners, to thoroughly research the doctors and the hospitals from which they are going to receive their care. Don't leave these things to chance and just assume it will be fine! Please don't make the mistakes like I did for the first couple of years of my care. I was completely naive and completely trusting of everyone in the medical field.

Turns out, not everyone in the medical field is skilled at what they do. Or, maybe some are skilled, but just don't have enough human compassion to do a superior job. I believe you have to truly care about people in order to have the desire to do an exceptional job. I am convinced that this applies in just about any type of work a person chooses, but especially in the medical field.

Not everyone is good at the job they chose, or maybe their personality is not suited for that field. It's not that you, as a patient, don't like those medical professionals or you wish anything bad for them, you just can't take your medical care that lightly when you are dealing with life and death issues like battling cancer. And that's what most cancer patients are dealing with at the time they are choosing their doctors and hospitals. I just don't want anyone to go through additional and unnecessary suffering like I did. This battle is tough enough on its own!

My husband and I got settled in to our new room. My husband had actually brought his Bi-Pap machine this time, so he could try and sleep during our stay at the hospital. He also brought his computer and ipad for work, and all the things he would need to attend meetings that were scheduled while I was admitted. He said he could do all his work here at the hospital and only leave me for planned meetings or specific appointments that could not be moved. I was extremely thankful that he has very flexible work and could get almost all of his work done as long as he has his computer.

The only disappointment we found was that there was no fold-away bed in my room for him. He would have to sleep on a recliner for the entire 3 weeks. That made me feel so bad for him. I can't imagine how uncomfortable that had to be for such an extended period. He said it was not going to be a big deal, even though I knew it had to be back wrenching. He never complained once. **How on earth did I get so blessed to with my awesome husband!**

My doctor, who was in charge of the clinical trial, came into my room after the nursing staff got me completely prepared for all the treatments. He explained that the first type of chemotherapy I would receive would be given for the first two days. When that was completed, I would start another type of chemotherapy which would be given for five days. That is seven days straight of chemotherapy! Whoa! He explained how these medications would basically wipe out the immune system.

Once my blood counts reached the number required by the study, they could then start the infusion of the Lymphocytes. He didn't want to waste any time, so I started the first chemotherapy that very first day. I was actually happy they started it that first day because I didn't want to waste any time either.

They gave me the chemotherapy that afternoon, and I unfortunately started to feel its effects pretty quickly. The nausea was terribly severe! They asked me if I wanted the several anti-nausea medications that I could receive via infusion into my port. I said yes to all of them! I hate being nauseated more than anything in the world! These medications not only reduced the nausea some, but they knocked me out completely. These medications were definitely more effective than the pill anti-nausea medications I had taken in the past.

This routine went on for two days. I would get the chemotherapy, and then I would start to feel very sick, and then the nurses would administer the anti-nausea medications that would make me **sleep A LOT**! When I was awake, I felt absolutely terrible, so I was all for the medications that would make me sleep as much as possible through these two horrendous days. I ate almost nothing for those two days. I believe they made me eat a couple of crackers just to take a pill each day. The nurses also tried to get me to drink as much water as possible. I truly felt like I never wanted to eat again. It was an extremely atrocious two days!

I was so happy when I was done with that first chemotherapy. I started on the second type of chemotherapy on Day 3. I couldn't believe the difference. I certainly didn't want to eat much, but I could at least hold a little food down with this medication. On a scale of 1 to 10, and 10 is horrendous, the first chemotherapy was a 10, but this chemotherapy was around a 3.

I felt like I had achieved some huge accomplishment. Knowing I was going to be on this second medication for five days seemed like a vacation in comparison. For the next five days, I was able to read and work on my computer and even work on some of the wedding plans while there.

While you are in the hospital, especially for something this serious, you have to get used to people coming in your room to check your vital signs quite often. There is a regimen that the nursing staff has to follow for the trial where they were required document your vital signs approximately every 3 hours or so. I certainly didn't mind because they were taking such good care of me. They also came in my room between 5-6 a.m. in the morning everyday to take blood. My blood work had to be done everyday.

We would look over the results of the blood work every morning when the doctor came in to explain my treatment for the day. The Lead Doctor of this entire trial was an extremely intelligent, kind and compassionate man. He was very knowledgeable about all the scientific background of this trial and had been working in this field a long time, but yet he took the time to thoroughly explain everything they would be doing each day. Plus, he made it simple enough that I could understand it. He usually had at least 3 other doctors with him. I discovered there is a sort of hierarchy of doctors in each department. The head doctor was my favorite. He was very empathetic despite having to explain this process to multiple patients!

My husband and I started to become pretty close to the nurses. It was completely different than going in to the hospital for a surgery or short procedure. With those, you are usually out of the hospital within 1-2 days. These were now people that you were talking to all day, everyday. Some of the treatments required constant monitoring, so your nurse was like your best friend. She would make sure you were tolerating all medications and she would order any additional medications needed and send it for approval from the doctors.

This particular part was also kind of embarrassing --- but they had to measure every cc of urine that came out of me. The medical team was required to track this to make sure I was not becoming dehydrated or had any blood in my urine. So they put this "hat-looking thing" on the commode to capture all urine. They would document it several times a day. Believe me, going to the restroom took some doing. I was hooked up to a ton of tubes. My chest port was connected to an IV that hung on a rolling IV pole. Also, they had sent me down to another floor in the hospital the second day I was there to get a picc line run in my arm. So, I had my picc line in my arm connected to an IV on the IV pole as well. Plus, they had a ton of sticker electrodes all over my body that were all hooked up to wires and to a portable battery unit that hung in my hospital gown pocket that constantly monitored my heart.

As you can imagine, this whole monstrosity was very easy to get tangled. And, it was quite difficult to drag this mess to the bathroom every time you had pee. It was like carrying several pieces of luggage to the bathroom. Plus, the bathroom was so small that the base of the IV pole didn't really fit into the bathroom well, so I had to have my husband stand guard every time I went in to pee to make sure no one opened the door to my room because it looked right into the bathroom. It had to be hysterical to watch me dragging all of this around every time I got out of bed.

After completing five days of chemotherapy, my doctor came in my room that next morning, Day 6, and told me that my lymphocytes were down to "0", so I didn't have to do the two extra days of chemotherapy, since we already hit the required goal. This was absolutely fabulous news! Anything that means less poison going in to my body was good news to me. It really worked out great because it was now the weekend and my family was wanting to come down to visit me, so I would feel a little more human-like during my visits. That was by far the best two days of my stay. It was really letting my body recover a little. And, I was so thrilled to see my children and their fiancés, and my brothers and their wives, and my parents and a couple of our closest friends. And, I know Norm would never say it, but I think he was probably thrilled to talk to someone other than me.

**Getting the Lymphocytes:**

I was so excited on Day 8 (September 19, 2017) because it was the day that would change everything. I would be receiving the IV that would deliver the new Lymphocytes (new immune system) that **would now recognize this hideous cancer in my lungs as an atrocious, foreign intruder and now attack it and kill it!**

The team of people that were in my room was amazing. This process had to be done with extreme precision. It was all very exciting. The lymphocytes were actually overnighted from the Research Company's Lab in a cooled case to keep them alive. There were extra nurses that came in on their day off just to watch it being done. I felt like a celebrity. We even took a few photos to commemorate the day. It all went perfectly. The nurses told me that I may run a fever later that day since my body was going to be working hard. I didn't even care. I was just thrilled at the thought that God had brought us to this place and I was going to be getting well...Finally.

This battle had been going on for over 6.5 years at this point. I probably thanked God for these people a hundred times that day. I did end up getting a fever later that day, as they predicted, but I just slept through it. Plus, my nursing staff was giving me medication to bring down the fever, so I really didn't feel that bad.

The day following the administration of the lymphocytes was an awful, agonizing day. I was required to receive a regimen of a special type of immune booster that would promote the growth of the lymphocytes. I'm sure this medication is very effective for the uses for which it was developed, but my body surely hated it. I was supposed to get six treatments of this medication over a three day period. When you hear the saying "ignorance is bliss", it definitely applies to me in this first administration of the drug.

I started off that day not nervous at all. They gave me a list of side effects I might encounter, but I was very hopeful I would not get any of them. No such luck. The nurses finished giving me the medication through my IV which was connected to my port. A very short time later, I started shaking. It's the same type of shaking you do when you are getting a fever. The nurses were telling me that this was normal to experience this shaking which is called "rigors". Over a period of approximately 5 minutes they had gone from moderate shaking to profoundly severe rigors that were probably 1000 x's worse than any previous rigors I had ever experienced from a fever in my entire life. Every muscle in my body had gone into a complete muscle spasm like a charlie horse, to the point where I could not even move my jaw to open my mouth. It was so clenched that I had no choice but to breathe out of my nose.

I can remember looking in my husband's eyes with complete fear and desperation. I could tell he felt really badly for me. I couldn't even speak to him because my jaw was completely clenched shut. This pain was so awful that I would definitely prefer childbirth to this. It's hard to describe the pain of feeling like every muscle in your body had a charlie horse. I'm sure everyone has experienced a charlie horse in their calf in the middle of the night and jumped out of bed to get rid of the pain. Well, imagine a pain like that in every muscle in your body. It was agonizing.

The nurse started to administer Demerol in small doses in my picc line to try and stop the rigors. They were only allowed to give me a small amount every 15 minutes. I'm sure there were very good reasons for this limitation. Fifteen minutes later the rigors were still going strong, so the nurse gave me another dose of the Demerol. Approximately 15 minutes later, the rigors started to subside. I don't think there is a word in the English language to describe how relieved I was that it was over. I fell asleep immediately from exhaustion and probably from the Demerol. It was probably the most intense workout I've ever done in my entire life. Imagine flexing every muscle you have until it goes into a muscle spasm for over a half hour.

I woke up about 30 minutes later and immediately threw up every bit of my breakfast. My body had never had experienced anything like Demerol before. It was obvious my body was rejecting it. Hands down, that was probably one of the worst experiences of my life!

When my Trial Doctor came back to my room later that day, he asked if I was ready for the second round of this medication. I envisioned me to running down the hall to the elevators and sprinting out of the building. I couldn't believe I was going to have to do this again. I told him how badly I reacted to it. He advised to start giving me the Demerol sooner to hopefully stop some of the rigors. So, I agreed to try it again.

Like before, the rigors started not long after they administered the drug in my IV. Sadly, the severity of the rigors was not any less. I writhed in pain for about 25 minutes this time. The Demerol being administered earlier may have shortened the time of the rigors by 5 minutes, but it certainly did not lessen the severity. Again, I fell asleep immediately afterward. And like clockwork, I woke up and threw up again.

After these two treatments, I felt like someone had sucked every ounce of life out of me. I felt like a little shell of a person. Stick a fork in me, because I was done. I spent the rest of the day napping and not moving or eating. I literally had nothing left!

This medication was the worst thing I had ever experienced-and I've experienced a lot of awful medicines! In the morning, my Trial Doctor came in to discuss the administration of this medication again. I was supposed to get 2 more doses that day. I literally broke down sobbing. I told him I didn't think I had it in me. Once I got a hold of myself and could again speak, I joked with him that I kind of preferred death over doing this again. He was a sweetheart of a man and he understood completely.

He explained that many people end up in the ICU after doing this medication. He asked me if I could do at least one more treatment. He thought 3 treatments would suffice since I had such an extreme reaction to the medication. I reluctantly agreed. Knowing what was coming was like complete torture. The nurses came in and started the infusion of the medication into my IV and I just kept telling myself that this was the last time I had to do this. I would never have to do it again! I kept thinking "last time" the entire time I while I was writhing in pain during the rigors. My husband kept reassuring me of this while he watched me suffering through this agonizing process again. When it was all over, I fell asleep again.

The next morning when my trial doctor came in and we were discussing my blood work, he showed me how low my hemoglobin had dropped. He told me that I was going to need some blood infusions. I could clearly see why it was very necessary. I had a new attitude on life though because I was still just so very elated that the agony part was over. I had been wondering why I was so weak though. I had to stop and take a break every time I walked across the room. The hemoglobin was definitely the reason.

It was now going to be a race to get my white cells to an acceptable level required by the trial before I could leave the hospital. Over the next few days, I received several infusions to combat my depleted blood. The chemotherapy had killed pretty much everything. I guess my condition was more serious than I thought, because no one could even come in my room without a mask during most of my stay in the hospital. Even the people who dropped off my meals, that were only in the room for about 30 seconds, had to put a mask on.

When that weekend finally came around, I was so excited to see my family again. Only a couple people had been able to come down during the week to visit me. One of my closest friends, that is a nurse came to visit several times during the week to check on my condition. She understood the severity of the treatments I was getting and just wanted to encourage me. And boy did I need it. My body was so much more beat up by that second weekend that I think everyone could see the difference. When my younger brother and his wife walked in, I actually broke down crying because I was so physically, emotionally, and mentally spent! Plus, I was so happy to see them! Everyone was completely masked up too. Looking back, I should have taken a photo of my entire family in my room wearing masks. It was hysterical looking.

Every morning, my trial doctor would come in, and every morning I would ask if my blood levels had reached the right number so I could go home. Finally, after 2 weeks and 1 day since being admitted, he gave me the thumbs up. He was really shocked that my numbers had gone up that quickly. I wasn't! I had been praying non-stop, the entire time I was in the hospital that God would get me out of there before the three weeks they told me I'd be there. As usual, God gave me great comfort the entire time I was in the hospital. My body was able to recover amazingly quickly. That was all I needed to hear from my doctor.

My nurse came in after the doctor left and I told her the good news. The doctor had already told her. She said there was going to be a lot of paperwork and other things that needed to be completed before I could actually leave the building. I had my bags packed in about 5 minutes and I was sitting in the chair next to my suitcase ready to go. Unfortunately, however, the nurse was right. We didn't get out of there until 1 p.m.

I wanted my husband to drive really fast all the way home. I texted every family member and close friend and told them the good news. It felt like I had been let out of prison. When you're not able to leave a room for over two weeks, it is very frustrating. They did occasionally let me walk the halls of my floor if I wore a mask, but only if my doctor ok'd it.    This was cabin fever like nothing I had ever experienced.

When we pulled into our driveway, I jumped out of the car and ran in the house like a lightning bolt to see my dog.  I know it sounds stupid to some people, but I really missed my dog!  I am a dog person for sure, and he is sort of like my little baby that will never grow up.   He must have thought I abandoned him since I was gone for so long.  While I was in the hospital, I was able to speak with my granddaughter and soon-to-be granddaughter quite often on the phone.  My soon-to-be son-in-law has an amazing daughter, so our family was growing quickly.   But now I couldn't wait to see both of them in person since we did not want them seeing me in the hospital while I was so sick.  Norm and I had such a great day.   I was rejoicing and thanking God all day!  Being at my home was suddenly like being on vacation.  I was just so thrilled to be in my own home.

## CHAPTER 13
## RECOVERY TIME AT HOME

---

Now that I was at home, all the monitoring of my symptoms had to be done by myself and my husband. And wow, was it nice to sleep in my own bed too! Everything I did at home was like a gift. Everything from showering to cooking my own food, and especially not having to measure all my urine. LOL! Even though I felt terrible, I was still so happy that I got to feel terrible at home.

The nurses had told me that running a low grade fever would be normal for a few weeks. They said to not be alarmed if I had a fever for a while. But, if I had a fever higher than 101F, then I was to call them. The fevers started almost immediately, I would wake up in the morning, and feel so tired that I would get a drink of water and grape juice, and then lay down and take another nap for 2-3 hours. I couldn't understand why I was so exhausted even after I just woke up in the morning.

Soon after, I figured I had better start monitoring my temperature, and it turned out to be the fevers and the low hemoglobin causing the exhaustion. I started taking my temperature several time a day, and I would watch it fluctuate from day to day. I would always take Ibuprofen or acetaminophen to bring the fever down and then I would feel better. This went on for weeks.

My blood counts for my hemoglobin were still extremely low when I left the hospital, but the doctor told me it would take time for that to go up. He warned me that I was going to feel weaker than I expected when I got home and it would last for several months. He explained how it would be worse at home because how I felt laying in a hospital bed is not going to be the same when I am at home trying to walk up and down stairs and moving around a lot more.

He was so, so right! I can remember the first time I tried walking up the steps to get to our main floor from the garage when we first got home. It was like lifting tree trunks for legs, even though I had just lost 15 lbs while in the hospital. I felt like crap constantly. Between the low hemoglobin, and the constant fevers, and the horrific coughing, I didn't feel like this was getting any better.

My cough had been getting progressively worse every month since October 2016. By the time I went into the hospital in September 2017, it had become a very normal occurrence for me to go into coughing fits every hour or two. I had become very skilled at calming the cough down. I would either run and get a piece of gum or get a hot cup of water to help ease the urge to cough.

If I was not able to get the coughing to calm down, my lungs seemed to go into an unstoppable spasm. It's very difficult to describe, because the longer it took me to stop the cough, the worse it would get...and I would eventually throw up. For the past year, I would throw up approximately 4-5 times a week. It usually depended on whether I had an active infection in there as well. Once I would get the infection to go away, then the coughing fits would occur a little less. But I would get infections often because of the humongous blockage in there.

So, in addition to my normal coughing, I was running a constant fever for close to a month. I was in no hurry to call the doctor like they had instructed me because I had absolutely no desire to go back into the hospital. I was dreading being away from home again. I know I was being stubborn, but I kept resisting my whole family's suggestion on this. Sorry everyone! My husband had been asking me to call the doctor for over a week when I finally gave in and called. This was approximately the third week of October.

I called the doctor "on call" and told her that I had been running a fever for almost a month and it was 102F. She was adamant that I should go to the Emergency Room. My breathing had become so labored and my cough had become so intense, that this time I did not hesitate to follow her instructions.

We arrived at the Emergency Room of the "Friendly" hospital that was closest to my home and I checked in. It did not take long for them to get me into a room in the E.R. The doctor came in and checked me out and said that I would need to get an X-Ray so he could look at my lungs. As soon as they got the results back, he explained that it looked like I had a pretty bad case of pneumonia and he wanted to get me on IV antibiotics as soon as possible. I was not shocked, but kind of happy that maybe I would feel a little better.

They got me into my own room upstairs very soon after and they started me on the antibiotics. I had been sick for so long and had trouble breathing every day for about the last year, so I think it had become hard for me to discern if my breathing had progressed to a worse state or has become infected, until it gets really bad. I know that is not a good thing, but it's sort of the nature of the beast when you have a condition where you have a difficulty breathing ALL THE TIME. I can't seem to differentiate between the different problems that are making my breathing difficult at that moment.

On the bright side, this hospital room was huge compared to the last hospital room I was in for over 2 weeks. And, they had a couch in the room that turned into a bed for my husband. He would actually get some sleep. This hospital was still fairly new, so the decor was very updated and pretty. It had a enormous window that looked out onto the 2nd busiest traffic intersection in Pennsylvania, so it had a ton of activity that I could watch whenever I wanted. Plus, I was only about 15 minutes from my house, so it would be so much easier for my friends and family to come and visit me.

The fact that we were so close to home now meant my poor husband could run home every morning and take a shower. Unlike at the last hospital, where he had to go down to the hallway bathroom to get washed up every morning and he only got to go home to shower when he could recruit someone to drive an hour to the hospital to sit with me while he ran home to shower. If I haven't made it clear before, I believe all spouses (including my husband) that are caring for their ailing spouses, really suffer and sacrifice much more than anyone knows. If the mental and emotional stress isn't enough, the physical stress, such as lack of sleep, is really hard on them.

If you know anyone taking care of a spouse with cancer or any other medical condition, please be supportive and try to give them a break once in a while. They never seem to complain, but it has to be brutal. I apologize often to my husband for what I put him through, and he always says the same thing, " You'd do the same thing for me."

I spent the next 4.5 days in the hospital. The hospital staff and doctors were great and I had constant visitors, so I did not have that feeling of isolation that I had during the last hospital stay. The staff was tracking my hemoglobin very closely because it had never really gone back up since I left the clinical trial. The doctor thought it would be good for me to get a couple of units of blood while I was there, since I was so extremely weak.

I had a fever and very difficult time breathing the first few days I was there. It was obvious I had really waited too long to go and seek medical attention. There was one night in particular, where I was struggling worse than usual to breathe. My husband was down the hall talking with some friends that had come to see him, and I was in the room, having a terrible time. I called him on his cell phone and asked if he could come and be with me because I couldn't believe how awfully I was struggling to breathe. He said goodbye to his friends and came right in. He and I immediately prayed. I remember praying with such desperation and asking God for His mercy and asked Him to relieve the stress in my breathing...it couldn't have been more than 3 minutes later that I coughed up a really big cancer nodule from my lung (one of the blobs). Wow, did that feel better!

I thanked God for like an hour. I can't even explain the relief. We called the nurse in and showed it to her. She asked if she could take it with her? I said, "Sure." She said she would be the hit of the nurse's station that night because her patient coughed up some of her cancer. We were all hysterically laughing. I was happy I could help make her night more interesting.

I got released from the hospital a couple of days later and was thrilled as always to go home. These days, I appreciate being at my home so much more. Just waking up in your own bed felt awesome. I couldn't get comfortable in a hospital bed, no matter how hard I tried. All the things in my house that usually bug me, like the fact that we need new flooring through the entire house, suddenly didn't seem like all that big of a deal. I still noticed all the house projects that needed to be completed, but I just figured I would get to them eventually.

I wanted to focus on the important things instead, like spending time with my family; and being able to jump in the car and go wherever I wanted 'at any time'. This probably will sound silly to most people because it was only

3 hospital stays. But, I believe the time in the hospital seems to make time go very slowly while you wait to be released. I don't know about other people, but this really made me appreciate "normal" life. It just made me not take as much for granted. Everyday that God gives me is a gift. I try and reflect on that every morning when I wake up and thank Him for the millions of blessings He has given me.

## Getting Ready for the Wedding:

After I got home from the hospital it was a race to get everything finished before my daughter's wedding. There were a bunch of things that had to be done at the last minute, but I gratefully got everything done in plenty of time. I had a ton of family and friends helping me make cookies. If you are not from Western Pennsylvania, you may not of heard of this, but here, you have to have a huge cookie table at a wedding. Standard Rule: 10 cookies per guest. My family and friends and I made approximately 2,000 cookies. There were almost 200 guests, so we figured we had better make that many cookies. We had a TON of cookies leftover though. I guess because there was so much regular food at the reception, people were too full to eat 10 cookies each. So, we were forcing people take cookies with them before they left the reception to go home. It was mandatory!

The week of the wedding was so fun. Preparing for everything was pure excitement. But, to put a little more stress in the week, I had been scheduled for a CT Scan the Monday before the wedding. The clinical trial called for a scan that particular week, **of course**. I went to the hospital and got the scan and saw the doctor and all seemed to be going well. Dr. Smart said he would call me later that week and give me the results. For the first time, I kind of did not want to know. I wanted to go to the wedding thinking everything was great. You know, the whole "ignorance is bliss" mentality. But, my doctor did call me a couple days later and read me the report. He said that there was no growth. This was fabulous news! Especially considering there was growth on every scan I had for the last two years. Now I could really celebrate at the wedding!

We had a wonderful time and it was definitely up there with one of my best days of my life! Just watching your daughter marry the love of her life was such an amazing blessing. And I was especially blessed that I was able to be there. I almost wanted to take a photo of me at the wedding and sent it to that doctor who  said I was supposed to be dead over 4 years ago.

The day after the wedding I was exhausted. I had been up really early on the wedding day and was still going strong at the reception all the way until after midnight. We finally got home and unpacked the car and went to bed around 2 a.m. This was a lot for me since I had just started getting my hemoglobin back up to close to the normal range.

Exactly 2 days after the wedding, I started getting sick. I had hugged and kissed and spoken to so many people at the reception, that it was not a surprise that someone would be carrying some kind of virus. Plus, like all weddings, everyone had to speak to each other by yelling our conversations because of the loud the music on the dance floor. It was similar to having a conversation at a concert. We were speaking to each other in close proximity to each other's faces, so everyone probably caught something. The head cold lasted for about a week until it moved to my lungs. So back I went to the local urgent care office to have them listen to my lungs and get me on another antibiotic. Ugh! I was so sick of being on antibiotics.

I probably made it another 3 weeks before I felt the next bronchitis coming on. The tumor in my left lower lung was so large that it was causing infections in my lungs probably about every 2 weeks at this point. I went on another round of antibiotics right before Christmas. Which worked out alright because I gratefully got to enjoy a really nice Christmas with my family.

I went to see Dr. Smart again in December 2017 as per the trial guidelines, and to get a CT Scan. All the bloodwork was getting better every time I went back, which meant my bone marrow was starting to repair and work well again since all the abuse it took during the chemotherapy I was given back in September for the trial. This was good news. My oncologist called me later that day with the results of the CT Scan and said that again, there was no growth of the cancer. Hooray!!! This was now 3 months with no growth. This was something that had not happened in a long time. He was very happy with those results and hoped that next scan would show shrinking in one of the tumors.

I have to reiterate that my "normal" without infection in my lungs still included constant coughing because of the large tumor in my lung. And along with constant coughing comes constant nose running. Not to mention that when I could not get the coughing fits to calm down, I would end up throwing up. Throwing up really makes my nose run and my eyes water like crazy, until I could get everything to calm down. I restate this because it had been over a year of constant coughing. It may sound like no big deal, but believe me, it is exhausting.

Coughing affects every second of my life. I can't go anywhere outside of my house without taking 3 Ibuprofen and chewing strong minty gum the entire time in order to lessen the amount of coughing that I do in a public place. It was also very embarrassing when I would go into coughing fits in front of people in public because sometimes the coughing fits still happen even with all the precautions I try and implement.

I am not saying any of this to feel sorry for myself. It is simply a fact of my life that has been going on since around October/November 2016, after the chronic pneumonia episodes. I had no idea back then that this would go on for so long. It is physically and emotionally exhausting. You would think that I would at least have ripped washboard abs by now, but no such luck!

**Allergic Reactions are Awful:**

In January of 2018, I had been given some prophylactic antibiotics and antimicrobial medications that I was supposed to take to prevent infections in my lungs. I remember not wanting to take any extra medication and resisting it. My husband insisted that it was important to take everything the doctor gave me because it was all part of the trial. I reluctantly took the medication and within an hour I had horrendous chills. And within 2 hours I had a fever of around 103F. My husband was obviously nervous because that was a really high fever. He would give me acetaminophen and then later Ibuprofen. With this regimen he was able to keep it under control. The fever lasted about 2 days, but I felt horrendous for an additional 2 days after that. I was so achy and tired that I couldn't get out of bed, and I had this horrible ringing in my ears. The entire reaction lasted close to 4 days, but it took about a week for the ringing in my ears to go away.

I told my husband that I thought that the whole thing may have been caused by one of the prophylactic medications, but he didn't think so and it was just a coincidence that my fever occurred at that time. So about a week later, I was feeling better and he told me I should keep on those medication since the doctor wanted me to take it to prevent infections, so I took it again. My body's reaction was exactly like before. Except this time my fever was up to 103.2 F. All of the exact same horrendous symptoms had returned, only a little worse. And, the ringing in my ears lasted over a week this time. This was awful!!!

Two weeks later, at the end January 2018, I went back to Dr. Smart for my scheduled checkup and for another CT Scan. I told him about the chronic bronchitis I was getting in my lungs and how I had been on so many antibiotics over the last few months. We discussed how he would keep monitoring my infections. He said to try to keep on the prophylactic medications that were part of the trial to prevent further infections. I told him I thought I might be having a severe reaction to one of the medications, but I wasn't positive. He said I should definitely let him know. He said there was a possibility I could have had a reaction to it because it was mixed with the other medications.

Which made total sense. I figured there was no way to be sure but to try taking it by itself. He then sent me down for the CT Scan and said he would call me later that day with the results.

After the scan, we went straight home. It was time for me to take my prophylactic  medications again to see if I had another reaction now that I was not on the other antibiotics. I took the medication once again because I had no real proof that these were the cause of the high fevers. Big mistake! I started getting the chills in less than an hour. Within 2 hours after that my fever was up to 103.5F. My reaction to this medication just kept getting worse each time I took it. There was now absolutely no doubt that this was a reaction to that specific medication!

The reaction was very severe. I believe that if you take a medication that you are allergic to over and over again, your body's reaction becomes more and more intensified  each time. At least it did with me. Now comes the even more awful part. I found out later, that sometimes when your body is going through a traumatic event like a really high fever or other negative things, your calcium carbonate crystals (also called otoconia) in your inner ear can become dislodged and make you so dizzy that you are extremely sick.

I believe the condition is called Benign Paroxysmal Positional Vertigo (or BPPV). Well, I was so nauseated and sick from this dizziness that I could not move off the couch for 5 days. Everytime I would get up to pee, I would get the most terrible vertigo and throw up. I was so dehydrated from the fever that I didn't get up much, so that was kind of a good thing. But I would also throw up every time I changed positions while sleeping because it would move the crystals. My husband and I did not know that this is what was going on. We just thought it was part of the medication reaction.

So, we let this go on for 5 days and finally decided to called our good friend that is a PCP. He explained what he thought was going on (the BPPV). He also explained a maneuver that you could do to get the crystals back in place. My husband watched several videos on the internet that showed how to perform the maneuver as well. I believe it is called the Epley Maneuver.

Norm had me lay down on the bed and he did exactly what he was shown to do on the video. Within about an hour, I started to feel better. I cannot tell you what a relief it was to come out of that. It was very traumatic for me because I had no idea what was going on and I was throwing up incessantly. Between the high fever and the constant throwing up, it was not my best 5 days, let me tell you.

Amidst the craziness of those 5 days, my oncologist did call my cell phone and spoke to my husband since I was way too sick to speak to anyone. He explained the results of the CT Scan. He said that the large tumor had stayed the same size, which was great news... but the really amazing news was that the smaller tumors had shrunk. **This was incredible!!!! The new immune system had kicked in. It was not only stopping growth, but it was now killing the cancer!!!**

I was so excited when my husband told me! Although it was probably hard for him to tell I was excited because I had a 103.5 fever at the time. I thanked God immediately! I knew that He had put me in touch with these wonderful people running this trial and it was now working!! If I had felt good when he told me, I probably would have gone out to celebrate with my family that night! Instead, I laid there for another 4 days with the vertigo. It was kind of a bummer that I didn't get to tell everyone. No worries though, because my husband made sure he told everyone. We were praising God for sure for my healing in progress!

Two months after this great news, I was having a very normal day. I was making dinner for my granddaughter, my son, and my dad. They had come over to visit. Around the time they were leaving, I walked them out to the car and waved goodbye, when suddenly I went into a coughing fit where I coughed up a really good sized blob (cancer nodule). I continued to cough and eventually coughed up another nodule, and then a third one. I was very excited because this was my body getting rid of the dead cancer. Especially since we now knew that my body had started to shrink the cancer.

Then I started to cough again, even harder, when suddenly I felt a nodule move, but nothing came out. It had become lodged in what must have been an important airway, because I was struggling terribly to get air, and I couldn't stop coughing. This went on for quite a while, when my husband decided he'd better take me to the Emergency Room to get some help in clearing this nodule from my airway.

When we arrived at this hospital, the Emergency Room staff was not sure how to handle this, so they sent me to another hospital. My doctor was out of town that week, so we had no way of getting him over to this hospital or even contacting him. We hoped we could get some help from another doctor since I just needed someone to unblock the airway. The hospital sent the pulmonologist "on staff" to talk to me since the problem was occurring in my lungs. I explained to her what had happened, but she told me that she did not agree with my explanation.

She said it was not a blockage from coughing up the cancer, but instead she told me she believed the cancer had grown and was now blocking my breathing and she was going to send Palliative Care to get me on pain control medication and on oxygen and then she would send me home (basically to go home and wait to die.) I told her that I had been completely fine prior to coughing up the large nodule that became lodged in my airway. I asked if she could use a scope to assist me in dislodging the blockage. She did not agree with me at all, and apparently she was the only person that had any say in the matter at this time at this hospital. My doctor was away and could not be reached, so I was at her mercy.

I laid there that entire day trying not to move, so that I could at least get a little air. I was basically panting and my oxygen was very low. That night, our friend from church came in to see how I was. He and my husband prayed over me and we knew God was in control of the entire situation and He would deliver me from it. The next morning, the Palliative Care Physicians Assistant came in to talk with me. I told her what happened as well, and she told me there was nothing their department could do to help me dislodge the nodule. She was just there to find out what they could do to ease my suffering. My husband and I told them how we knew the Lord would take care of this situation even though we were not being helped by the Pulmonologist.

I could see she felt badly that I was struggling so hard to breathe. She was extremely kind and told me she would return later that day, after she filled out all the paperwork for my case, and would bring the Palliative Care Physician to talk with me. All of the hospital personnel I had spoken to had told me that same thing. There was no way for me to get a second opinion about my lungs while I was there. The respiratory therapist had also come in to try and help me get more oxygen because mine was so low. Finally, I decided I just needed to get out of there and make an appointment with another pulmonologist and ask them to try and dislodge this chunk of cancer.

The next morning, I asked my husband to assist me in getting to the shower since I was so low on oxygen. He turned on the water and got everything ready for me, and as soon as I stepped in the shower and breathed in the steam, I went in to a really violent coughing fit. I started coughing up a bunch of blood and mucus, and then I suddenly coughed up the largest cancer nodule I had ever seen. It was such an amazing relief. I could instantly breathe normally again. I was thanking Jesus big time for answering our prayer!

About ten minutes later the Palliative care team came to my room. They had come back to finalize some paperwork. The P.A. that had been with me earlier that morning was floored. She couldn't believe that I was up and walking around and packing my bags and breathing freely. I was completely back to normal. She explained to the Palliative

Care Physician that this was not even the same person that had been lying there struggling to breathe earlier.

I took them in and showed them the large nodule laying on the shower floor that I had repeatedly told everyone was blocking my airway. I left it in the shower so I could show the Pulmonologist. The Palliative team was amazed at the size of it. My husband and I were very thankful for what God had done and for sending this Palliative Care group. Norm asked them if they would like to pray with us? They actually said ok --- so Norm prayed and thanked God for delivering me from this blockage and for this caring team of professionals.

I also showed my nurse the nodule when she returned to my room. She was also shocked at how big it was. The Respiratory Therapist came back and checked my oxygen and it was now back to normal as well. I told the resident on duty that I was ready to go home. Not shockingly, the pulmonologist never came back to see me before I left.

As I have reiterated many times throughout the book...**don't let people discourage you.** They are just people. We are all fallible and capable of being wrong ... very wrong. (I'm wrong about things all the time... just ask my husband). And we have seen that some doctors and medical personnel are not as caring at their job as others, or they just aren't as skilled. So, don't accept things blindly.

## CHAPTER 14
## THE BATTLE IS COMING TO AN END

---

As of this writing, I have currently been battling cancer for over 7.5 years and I still sit back sometimes and think that it's just so hard to believe that this fight has been going on so long for me. You would think that because I have been dealing with it for such a long period of time I would be used to it, but it still has a surreal aspect in my mind. Maybe it's me just wanting it to be done. I have been fighting for so long! I know that I have depended on God every single day for strength for sure!

When someone you know is going through a battle with cancer, it's important to keep in mind that even though they are constantly trying to remain positive and putting on a brave face in front of the world, it's a very wearying thing to deal with day, after day, after day. Coping with the onslaught of symptoms from the cancer on your body is exhausting. Not to mention, the very intense side effects of the chemotherapy, and radiation, and surgery really does wear on you physically, mentally and emotionally as well. The spouses, and family members, and the close friends that are in constant contact with the person who is battling cancer play a very important role in keeping their mental attitude in the right place.

It's important for those who are closest to us to give encouragement and stay positive. It's best to stay focused on what we know God wants for us --- He wants us to live a joy-filled life that He has provided and focus on His unending grace. But every once in a while, the spouse/family member will probably have to extend some additional grace to the patient that is battling the cancer. Especially if the person is having a weak moment. Just lovingly direct them back to the Word of God and His promises, and that He wants them healed.

Sometimes we need to have an outlet for the pain and weariness. Sometimes you just want to ventilate or cry. Having a righteous anger toward the cancer is healthy! This evil thing has no right to be in my body! Command that piece of crap to leave your body!

I know personally that I sometimes get overwhelmed with just being physically exhausted from fighting the many symptoms which I fight everyday. My husband has learned that it's good to just let me get out my frustration or just cry out the pain once in a while. **Then, I get right back on track with that positive mental attitude of: This evil thing is Dying by the Power of Jesus Christ! He paid the price for all our sickness and disease. We just have to believe in His sacrifice and receive our healing.**

(Mark 11:24 KJV) "Therefore I say unto you, What things soever ye desire, when ye pray, believe that ye receive them, and ye shall have them."

I could not write my story without letting everyone reading this know how much I depend everyday on my relationship with God to sustain me and give me strength. I think that is probably quite obvious if you've just read my story. Through the intense research my husband has done about healing and sickness in this world, we have studied the plethora of passages in the bible (in the new and old testaments) that detail how sickness and disease all started at the fall of man. God originally made our environment perfect. Man and woman chose to sin and therefore gave the dominion of the earth over to satan. He is the author of all evil in this world. If we study the bible in its original language, it is quite clear that God cannot even look on sin, or on sickness and disease, which is part of sin. **Which is why He sent His Son to purchase our deliverance, and paid for our sins and sicknesses IN FULL!**

Therefore, no one can say that God is responsible for any suffering in this world. I lean on Him everyday for strength and believe He has healed me from this horrendous disease that satan put on me to try and destroy my faith.

I believe that Jesus paid the price for not only our sins, but has also paid the price for all of our healing. He prophesied this in His Word in the Old Testament:
(Isaiah 53: 5 KJV) "But he was wounded for our transgressions, he was bruised for our iniquities: the chastisement of our peace was upon him; and with his stripes we are healed."

Then in the New Testament He told us about our healing in the past tense, because our sicknesses had already been paid for by Jesus Christ:
(1 Peter 2:24 KJV): "Who his own self bare our sins in his own body on the tree, that we, being dead to sins, should live unto righteousness: by whose stripes ye were healed."

Jesus healed every single person that came to him for healing when he was on this earth. And when the Leper came to him for healing in Luke 5:12, he asked if it was His will to heal him. And Jesus responded:
(Luke 5:13 KJV) "And he put forth his hand, and touched him, saying, I will: be thou clean. And immediately the leprosy departed from him."

That is the beautiful part of studying the healing done by Jesus. It was always His will to heal everyone that asked Him for healing. So therefore, everyone who desires to receive their healing, must believe in their heart that Jesus Christ has paid the price for their healing and pray to receive their healing through faith in their Lord and Savior and Healer, Jesus Christ.

True faith is the way to receiving your healing. "Unwavering Faith" to be exact. Which is why it is the title of this book!

(James 1:6 KJV) "But let him ask in faith, nothing wavering. For he that wavereth is like a wave of the sea driven with the wind and tossed."

Just as fervently and assuredly I believe that Jesus Christ has paid the price for my Salvation and that I am going to heaven after this life; I also fevently and assuredly believe that Jesus Christ has paid the price for all my sickness and disease and that He has healed me!!!

I would not be true to myself if I didn't at least give all the readers of this book the information and truth needed to believe on Jesus Christ as their Savior as well. It is not a difficult thing to do.

You can simply pray:

**Father in heaven, I am believing on Jesus Christ, your Son, as my Savior. I believe that you sent Him to this earth to die on the Cross to pay the price for my sins, and that I could never pay for them on my own. I believe Jesus arose three days later victorious over sin. I pray this in the name of Jesus, Amen.**

(John 3:16 KJV) For God so loved the world that He gave His only begotten Son, that whosoever believeth in Him should not perish, but have everlasting life.

(Romans 10:9 KJV) That if thou shalt confess with thy mouth the Lord Jesus, and shalt believe in thine heart that God hath raised Him from the dead, thou shalt be saved.

If you have prayed this prayer and believe, I am happy to tell you, that you are on your way to heaven. You are a child of the King and today is your Spiritual Birthday. Now would be a good time to find a church that is teaching the "Good News" about Jesus and to grow in your walk with Him. Growing in your walk with God is very important so that you can live a victorious and joyful life.

My husband always shares these statements with new Christians:

When I renew my mind with God's Word (the Bible), It transforms my heart.

When I transform my heart, I change my actions.
When I change my actions, I change my results.
– My desires become His desires!

(Romans 12:2 KJV) "And be not conformed to this world: but be ye transformed by the renewing of your mind, that ye may prove what is that good, and acceptable, and perfect, will of God."

I hope every reader has enjoyed reading my story, or at least learned something that will make your life better. I am obviously not proclaiming to be a medical professional in this book, I simply want others to have an easier road in their journey to becoming cancer-free than I had.

I'm sure I will have many more victories to celebrate as I continue to watch God work mightily in my life.

As I wrap up the final thoughts in this book, I wanted to share an amazing thing that happened to my husband not that long ago that strengthened our faith even more. But, I'm going to let him write this part since it was his experience: (Norm speaking)

I was on my way to the pharmacy to pick up Rachele's prescriptions for her antibiotics. On the way there, which was only a few miles from the house, I heard a voice from behind, it wasn't an audible voice but internal voice that I have heard many times in my life. I have built up a sensitivity to hear when the Lord is speaking to me. The voice said, "From now on, you shall call her Raphaela." I spoke out loud and said, "Why would I call her Raphaela?" I have never called her that my entire life, she has a beautiful name, Rachele.

A little backstory--- my wife was named after her great grandmother from Italy Raphaela . They Americanized her name to Rachele. For her entire life, her dad would refer to her a lot as Raphaela. So, to me, when I heard that God wanted me to call her this I thought he was referring to an Italian name. So very confused, at the next stop light... I quickly looked up the meaning of the name Raphaela on Google. I was clearly expecting to see a definition related to an Italian name, but I was very shocked when I saw the true meaning. The name Raphaela wasn't even Italian, it was Hebrew, and the amazing part was it actually means "God has healed"! As soon as I saw that I started crying. I finally made it to my destination at the pharmacy and walked around the isles very perplexed. I was trying to process all this. What did this mean...that from now on I shall call her Raphaela, God has healed. I called my wife and told her what had happened and immediately she cried as well with joy. Still to this day, every opportunity I can, I call her Raphaela as God has declared it... God has healed her.

(Back to me speaking):

He is absolutely right. I AM most definitely Raphaela! **God has healed me**!!

If you would like to share your inspirational story, or what has helped you the most in your battle with cancer, or for more information, please visit RacheleWright.com.

# A MESSAGE TO MY AMAZING FAMILY!

There is no way I could write this and not thank the incredible family God has blessed me with. I know it has not been easy to watch all of these difficult circumstances occur in our lives, but you all have dealt with them with unimaginable strength and grace. These simple words will never properly express how I feel about each one of you in my heart!! I love you all so much!!!

Where do I begin when describing my husband? I could never fully describe the immovable bond that we have and how we still manage to become even closer every day of our lives thanks to God being the center of our marriage. You've just read first-hand how this story wouldn't even have played out this awesome if it wasn't for the fierce love my husband has for me, and his relentless research on healing, and his uncompromising belief in God's Word. The poor man has been through the ringer because of me and has never complained once. I hate that I put him through so much. I know how blessed I am to have such a wonderful, loving, creative, intelligent, God-loving, and protective husband. We are still having fun together 29 years later and we still laugh and enjoy spending time together everyday. I know for a fact that I would have never made it through this journey without him. I thank God for him everyday. I love you Norm!

My son is my first born child and we have always been extremely close. I think he was the only young man that wasn't embarrassed to hug his mom in front of his friends in high school. We have always been able to talk about just about anything. That's not the most common thing with a mom-son relationship. He has always been an exceptional athlete, and a talented, handsome, funny and loving person, but I was always thankful for how he always made his family first priority. Not to mention that he became a father at a very young age and amazed me at how quickly he grew up and became a responsible, patient, devoted, loving and hard working father. He is a born leader and has that smile that lights up a room and can charm anyone. I thank God for my son everyday. I love you Brennan!

I love and adore my amazing, beautiful, loving, hard working and incredible daughter. She has always been so naturally intelligent, like her dad, that she barely even had to study in school and still did well. She has a dynamic, funny and magnetic personality and everyone that has ever met her, loves her. She is absolutely gorgeous and doesn't know it. She has always had great discernment about right and wrong, even in those crazy teen years, that I never had to worry too much about her choices. I knew she would want to do God's will. Plus, she is very multi-talented and she never stops making me laugh. I love it that she can imitate anyone and sound just like them or do any accent and it sounds perfect. I am so blessed and thankful to have her as my best girlfriend in the world! I thank God for her everyday. I love you Laney!

My granddaughter was the first baby born in our family in a long time, and she had all four adults in our house wrapped around her little finger. Since my son became a single dad very young, we all got to spend a lot of time with her since he lived at home with us the majority of her life. This was a huge blessing to all of us since my husband and I love spending time with our family more than anything else in life. There's nothing better than having your children and grandchildren around.

I love spending time with my granddaughter, and she and I have always had a very close Grammy and granddaughter relationship. I believe we will always have that special bond because she lived at our home for so long. She had so many years of being the only grandchild that I don't think there is a child alive that got as much love and attention as her. She is so kind, and loving, and intelligent, and funny and beautiful. Her and I love doing a lot of the same things, and we both really love animals. We always have so much fun together. I am so blessed and thankful that I got to become her Grammy so young! I thank God for her everyday! I love you my Sweetie!

Since I started writing this book, we've had many wonderful additions to our little family. My son started the joyful stream of announcements by proposing to his girlfriend on their anniversary of one year of dating. I remember the day so vividly because none of the surprises my son arranged went as planned, which made the day even more fun and spontaneous. Both families joined them right after the surprise to celebrate how happy we were that they found each other.

About 3 months later, my daughter and her boyfriend of 6 months got engaged. No one was surprised when her fiancé had previously went to my husband for permission to propose, because we all knew they were meant to be. That was another night of absolute joyous celebration with both families. They got married approximately 6 months later, and had a baby right away. My son and his fiance decided to wait until 2018 to get married.

Both weddings were some of the most happy days of my life. I actually knew that both of my children were marrying the person that God had picked for them because He had brought them together through really ironic circumstances. I remember looking at my son-in-law's face when he watched my daughter coming down the aisle. They both were just beaming because you could see how much they loved each other. Fast forward to my son's wedding and I got to see my son struggling to keep it together when he saw his beautiful bride coming down the aisle. I don't think there's a more peaceful and content feeling for a parent than knowing that their children are with the right spouses.

My daughter-in-law is truly the only person I ever thought was the right person to marry my son. She has that exceptional personality where you can truly see she cares about others and wants to make a difference in the world. She is an awesome professional dancer and is super creative and smart. I'm sure her thoughtfulness, kind heart and love for the Lord are what drew my son to her. She is beautiful inside and out and I thank God for her everyday. I love you Rudy!

My son-in-law is the exact person I prayed for, for my daughter. Knowing how much my husband loves and respects me, I certainly wanted the same thing for my daughter. There are so many similarities in our relationships, it is sort of funny. He is handsome, kind, responsible, smart, hard-working and loving. Most importantly, he loves God with all his heart and it is obvious he wants to do God's will in caring for his family. He brought his precious daughter into our family at age 9, and even though we all were not around for the beginning years of her life, we could not love her more than if she was born in to our family. She is a beautiful child with a beautiful heart and she is way more mature than any child her age. It's crazy how intelligent she is and she blows me away with her adult-like questions about life. I thank God everyday for them! I love you Jeremy and my Sweetie #2.

I have already told the wonderful story of how I got to be in the delivery room with my daughter, but I also must convey how special it is to see your grandchild come into this world. When I delivered my own children, I was in way too much pain to really see what was going on down there, and really had no desire to see it. But fast forward 25 years and watch your daughter deliver her child, and it's an absolute miracle! My new granddaughter is still only a baby, but I cherish every moment I get to spend with her. She already smiles constantly and actually shakes when she laughs because she gets so excited. Her beautiful face and smile make my heart melt. I thank God for her everyday! I love you my Sweetie #3!

Made in the USA
Coppell, TX
05 July 2020